35444003148540

j 13: ..... SUT

Su

Ha  es

D1533633

HAUNTED
CANADA 7
CHILLING TRUE TALES

HAUNTED CANADA 7

CHILLING TRUE TALES

JOEL A. SUTHERLAND

Illustrations by
Norman Lanting

Thompson-Nicola Regional District
Library System
300 - 465 VICTORIA STREET
KAMLOOPS, B.C. V2C 2A9

Scholastic Canada Ltd.
Toronto New York London Auckland Sydney
Mexico City New Delhi Hong Kong Buenos Aires

Scholastic Canada Ltd.
604 King Street West, Toronto, Ontario M5V 1E1, Canada

Scholastic Inc.
557 Broadway, New York, NY 10012, USA

Scholastic Australia Pty Limited
PO Box 579, Gosford, NSW 2250, Australia

Scholastic New Zealand Limited
Private Bag 94407, Botany, Manukau 2163, New Zealand

Scholastic Children's Books
Euston House, 24 Eversholt Street, London NW1 1DB, UK

www.scholastic.ca

Library and Archives Canada Cataloguing in Publication

Sutherland, Joel A., 1980-, author
Haunted Canada 7 : chilling true tales / by Joel A. Sutherland
; illustrations by Norman Lanting.

Issued in print and electronic formats.
ISBN 978-1-4431-4881-8 (softcover).--ISBN 978-1-4431-4882-5 (HTML)

1. Ghosts--Canada--Juvenile literature. 2. Haunted places--
Canada--Juvenile literature. I. Lanting, Norm, illustrator II. Title.
III. Title: Haunted Canada seven.

BF1472.C3S987 2017   j133.10971   C2016-907988-0
                                                C2016-907989-9

Cover credits:
Photo © grapestock/Fotolia.

Interior border: Shutterstock © Filipchuk Oleg.
Illustrations by Norman Lanting.

Text copyright © 2017 by Joel A. Sutherland.
Illustrations copyright © 2017 by Scholastic Canada Ltd.
All rights reserved.

No part of this publication may be reproduced or stored in a retrieval system, or
transmitted in any form or by any means, electronic, mechanical, recording, or
otherwise, without written permission of the publisher, Scholastic Canada Ltd.,
604 King Street West, Toronto, Ontario M5V 1E1, Canada. In the case of photo-
copying or other reprographic copying, a licence must be obtained from Access
Copyright (Canadian Copyright Licensing Agency), 56 Wellesley Street West,
Suite 320, Toronto, Ontario M5S 2S3 (1-800-893-5777).

6 5 4 3 2 1   Printed in Canada   139   17 18 19 20 21

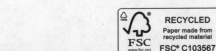

3 5444 00314854 0

For Fiona. Never stop smiling.

INTRODUCTION

When it comes to ghost story hunting, sometimes you're in the right place at the right time. Or, if you're easily spooked and dislike the thrill of a good ghost story, I suppose that would be the wrong place at the wrong time. But since you're reading this, I suspect you're like me and you love to be scared.

One day not too long ago, a woman named Toni came into the library where I work, looking for some help. As you might expect, the typical library customer asks for book recommendations or needs help with homework assignments or finding information about their community. But Toni had a different request — a dark, disturbing request.

She wanted to find information about the history of her house.

It was — as you might have guessed by now — haunted.

Toni was quickly put in touch with me (after writing the three previous volumes of *Haunted Canada* and *Summer's End*, I've become something of a ghost expert). What she told me about her house was, in a word, horrifying. The walls were crammed with restless spirits: ghosts that taunted her nearly every night, spectres that attacked her son, paranormal entities that drove nearly everyone away. Yet Toni had lived in the house for more than twenty-five years. I had to ask her why she hadn't left.

Her answer spread a chill up and down my spine. I needed to know more.

Fortunately, Toni agreed to meet up later so I could interview her about her experiences. I've conducted many interviews with people who have had haunting encounters over the years, but nothing prepared me for the story Toni shared that day. It was the single most terrifying account of a haunted house I have ever heard, and I've heard plenty.

The events Toni shared with me during that interview appear in this book in a chapter titled "You Can Never Leave." It's longer than most of the other stories because I couldn't leave out any of the terrifying details. I still get goosebumps when I think back on the disturbing images that were conjured in my mind while Toni told me about her house.

I enjoy writing about well-known landmarks and buildings that are haunted, like Old City Hall in Toronto or the Centaur Theatre in Montreal. It's fun to know that I can visit these locations myself and hopefully catch sight of a spectre or two. But I will confess that my favourite stories to write are about private homes, and are based on original interviews that I've personally conducted. As I travel across Canada and speak to readers in schools and libraries, I almost always hear from at least one or two people who share with me (some in a hushed whisper, others loudly and proudly) that their house is haunted. I've come to believe that there's something therapeutic in telling someone who believes in ghosts that ghosts live in your house.

Is your house haunted? You might want to try sharing your story with someone. You could write your own account, like the true stories you'll find in this book. Maybe doing so will give you a little peace. Or perhaps you'll find some comfort in reading about what other people have gone through. But fair warning: some of the stories — like Toni's — might make you even more terrified to turn out the lights at night.

Frightfully yours,

Home Sweet Horror

London, Ontario

Sabrina was an avid reader. From a very young age, she was often found with her nose buried in a good book, and she enjoyed finding comfortable reading nooks in quiet, private places. But in all of the travels she took to faraway lands and make-believe places, she never encountered any place half as terrifying as her own home.

When Sabrina was five years old, she climbed up the rickety stairs that led to the attic of her family's old house on Princess Avenue in London.

With a copy of the latest Junie B. Jones book in hand, Sabrina hid among the family's storage items and began to read in peace and quiet, alone.

But that wasn't completely accurate. The attic might have been peaceful and quiet, but she wasn't alone.

When Sabrina looked up from her book, she was surprised to see another girl in the attic. She appeared to be about fifteen years old and was standing in a shadowy corner on the other side of the room, silently watching Sabrina read. Her hair was curly, long enough to reach her waist and such a bright shade of red that it looked like her head was wreathed in flames. Something in the redhead's expression made it clear that she was extremely lonely.

"What's your name?" Sabrina asked, not afraid of the teenage girl.

The redhead didn't answer Sabrina's question. Instead, she continued to stare at Sabrina from the shadows.

With growing sympathy for the older girl, Sabrina asked, "Do you want to play with me?"

The redhead answered not with words, but with a wide grin. And then, without having uttered a single word, she disappeared.

Years passed and Sabrina wondered whether the red-headed ghost had been a figment of her imagination. But then late one night, when Sabrina was eleven, she dozed off while reading. This wasn't unusual. What was unusual was that she had fallen asleep in the rec room in the basement and woken up standing in the dark attic. She figured she must have been sleepwalking. She crossed the room, gripped the doorknob and turned it. It didn't budge. The door was locked. But that didn't make sense — there was no lock on either side of the door. It felt as if someone was holding the door closed, trapping her in the attic. Sabrina tried opening the door more forcefully. It still didn't open. She banged on its wooden panels and screamed at the top of her lungs. No one heard her, not even her parents.

The window, Sabrina thought desperately. She raced across the attic and tried to push the sole window open, but something held it in place too.

That's when she heard a faint whisper behind her. Even before she turned around, she had a feeling where she would find the source of the quiet sound. Sure enough, the ghost was standing in the same corner where she had spotted her six years before. She still had her distinctive curly red hair, but her face, hands and legs were covered in burn scars, leading Sabrina to believe the teenage girl had died in a horrible fire.

She stared at Sabrina in silence and then flashed a wide grin and disappeared, just as she had done before. The attic door immediately swung open. Sabrina wondered if, instead of sleepwalking, the spirit had possessed her body and led her to the attic. The more she considered this, the more convinced of it she became. But she couldn't fathom why.

The ghost didn't wait another six years before reappearing, nor did she feel the need to remain in the attic. One summer morning when Sabrina was thirteen, she slowly woke up then grew alarmed — she couldn't move a muscle. It felt like someone very strong was holding her down. More than that, it felt like her body had been encased in cement.

Although she could still open her eyes, she probably wished she hadn't. Lying in bed beside her was the red-head, her skin once again covered in burns. She looked like she wanted to speak, but instead of words, blood ran out of her mouth and then she disappeared.

After this horrific encounter, the ghost haunted Sabrina more regularly. For the next three weeks she peered out of alcoves and followed Sabrina around the house. One day, Sabrina looked in the bathroom mirror and realized with a swell of panic that her reflection was beginning to resemble the redhead. Every time she looked in the mirror she looked a little less like herself and a little more like the spirit.

Over the years, the ghost has continued to terrify Sabrina. The redhead appears, grins and disappears. The next day she appears, grins and disappears. And again she appears, grins and disappears. Sabrina has come to believe that the ghost is no longer haunting her house; the ghost is haunting *her.*

Sabrina doesn't know the ghost's name. She doesn't know where, when or how she died. She doesn't know why she has chosen to haunt her house or her soul. But she does know this: the redheaded ghost's intentions don't feel innocent or benign. Sabrina is convinced that it's only a matter of time before the ghost does something truly terrible to her, and she hopes she can figure out a way to stop her before it's too late.

DEAD MAN WALKING

Victoria, British Columbia

A woman entered Helmcken Alley one sunny afternoon. She was passing through on her way to nearby Bastion Square, lost in her thoughts, when a man suddenly appeared in front of her, blocking her path. He wore a grey canvas jacket and matching pants that the woman recognized as an old prison uniform. The skin on his face was sallow and pulled tight over his skull. His hair was dishevelled and his eyes were sunken. He staggered toward her, and with every step he took the woman heard the rattling of heavy chains. She looked down at his ankles and saw that they were shackled by a thick chain that dragged along the ground between his feet. Without a word he reached out his hands, which were also shackled.

The woman turned and ran back the way she had

come. Her only relief was the knowledge that she'd be able to outrun a man whose ankles were chained together.

But then, just as she neared the end of the alley she had entered, the man appeared again, directly in front of her. How could that be? He hadn't passed her. She screamed and turned once more. Fearing for her life, the woman sprinted as fast as she could and kept her head down, too afraid to look up. She ran and ran and didn't stop until she left the alley and reached the middle of Bastion Square. When she peered back into the alley, it was empty.

The man she had seen was the infamous Ghost of Helmcken Alley. He had been a member of a chain gang in the 1860s and had been sentenced to death by Sir Matthew Begbie, a man who earned the nickname the Hanging Judge and who today haunts the nearby Maritime Museum. On the day of his execution, the prisoner was to be led by a guard from the old provincial courthouse and jail to the gallows in Bastion Square, where Victoria's public executions took place. The guard, however, had some personal beef with the prisoner and beat him to death in Helmcken Alley.

Today the prisoner's ghost assaults the living who wander into his haunt, like the woman who was chased up and down the alley. Others have heard unexplained tolling bells, shattering glass or disembodied screams, while some have been afflicted by sudden headaches or felt hands grab their legs and arms from behind.

It has been said that the dead cannot cry out for justice, but this doesn't hold true in Helmcken Alley. The dead man there — forever peeved about his conviction and demise — is quite capable of making an unholy racket for all to hear.

THE LOCKED DOOR TO THE THIRD FLOOR

Winnipeg, Manitoba

One summer during high school, Kendra Vyse worked at the McBeth House, a seniors' drop-in centre that was also used for a few other purposes. But she never felt truly comfortable in the large house, especially not when she was alone.

Kendra didn't enjoy being on the second floor; it gave her a bad feeling. And the third floor? Forget it. Kendra avoided it like the plague. She kept herself busy on the main floor, where she didn't feel quite so uneasy. When she was alone and needed to clean the second floor, she would race upstairs, work quickly and speed back down before anything bad could happen. When other people were there with her, she didn't feel as anxious or afraid.

One day, she and her grandfather, who had helped to save the building from demolition, were the only two people on the property. They were outside when he asked her to return a child's car seat, which had been used for a weekly course for new parents, to the third floor of the building.

Although she didn't particularly want to, Kendra went inside and made her way up the stairs toward the attic. She paused at a door that led to the third floor. The door had to be locked at all times due to a fire regulation, so Kendra fumbled with the key in one hand while holding the car seat in her other arm. With trembling fingers, she fit the key in the lock, turned it and opened the door. Then she went upstairs. It was dark and dusty. The air was musty and still. Among the stored items were stacked boxes and piles of old McBeth family records and local history files. Kendra was overcome with an uncomfortable sensation and a feeling of dread, but she managed to return the car seat to its proper place and leave as quickly as possible, making sure to lock the door behind her.

She felt lucky to have escaped the third floor without incident, despite the terrible feeling she'd had. Her luck would not last a second time.

The McBeth family was among the Red River colony that emigrated from Scotland in 1815 and settled the land that is part of present-day Winnipeg. There was much bloodshed in the settlement in those early days as competing interests vied for control of the land. But the McBeths retained their property and turned their original log cabin into a larger red house.

McBeth House

Kendra was aware of the property's history, and equally aware of the treasure trove of information that was locked away in the attic. An idea for a novel based on the early history of the area entered her head and wouldn't leave her alone. If only she could spend some time up there — just a little — to research her idea, she was certain she'd find what she needed to write an incredible book. But try as she might, she couldn't shake the horrible feeling she'd had that time with the car seat, nor the unease she felt on the second floor.

She tried to convince herself that maybe she was just imagining things. After all, nothing had actually happened when she'd ventured all the way up the last time.

Finally, she made up her mind. She got the key. She walked up to the second floor. But as she stood before the door to the third floor, about to put the key in the lock, a terrible feeling washed over her. It was worse than anything she'd ever experienced in the McBeth House. It was an evil presence and it was very, very angry.

No research, no matter how valuable, was worth facing whatever it was that dwelled above. Kendra quickly turned and fled, practically running down the stairs back to the relative safety of the first floor. But as she retreated, the evil presence pursued her. She felt certain it was a man, but she had no idea why he was so enraged by her presence. Without warning he suddenly lashed out and pushed her from behind, trying to make her fall down the stairs. Fortunately, Kendra managed to stay on her feet and run out of the house before the man could do anything worse to her.

Kendra kept her job at the McBeth House until her summer contract ended, but she never went upstairs alone again. In fact, it was a struggle to work up the courage to go upstairs even when accompanied by someone else. And she never retrieved the documents she had hoped to study for her novel, which remained unwritten. Whoever, or whatever, lurks on the third floor has taken it upon himself to guard the information that lies therein.

GRAVEYARD OF THE ATLANTIC

Sable Island, Nova Scotia

Captain Torrens of Halifax's 29th Regiment of Foot bowed his head and covered his face to keep the blowing sand out of his eyes, nose and mouth, then trudged into the howling winds of the Atlantic Ocean. It was an uncomfortable journey to say the least, but he needed to spend some time alone with his trusted canine companion to clear his mind. Behind him, the few men of his crew who had survived the shipwreck set about the grim and morbid task of burying their dead fellow crewmembers.

The captain was investigating the 1799 sinking of the *Francis*. The Duke of Kent, Commander-in-Chief of British forces in North America, had sent the *Francis* to the New World loaded with many of his personal items and carrying key personnel in advance of his own journey across the Atlantic. But the *Francis* sunk off the coast of Sable Island, and most of the people on board died immediately. Some survived and washed up on shore only to be murdered before they had enough time to get to their feet. It was rumoured that pirates killed those who survived the *Francis's* sinking, while some claimed it was the island's ghosts that did the killing. It was a grim irony that Captain Torrens's ship, the *Harriet* — the gun brig sent to discover what had happened to the *Francis* — was also shipwrecked off the coast of Sable Island.

The captain's ship and the *Francis* were not the only vessels wrecked on what sailors called the Graveyard of the Atlantic. More than 350 shipwrecks have been recorded on Sable Island since 1583, and thousands of people have died there. Those numbers might actually be much higher if unrecorded tragedies could be added in. Some sources figure more than 500 ships have been destroyed there, and peg the death toll at ten thousand. The island, which is not much more than sand, grass and one lonely pine tree, is curved in a crescent shape that resembles a wide, mischievous grin. Seals, birds and more than 350 wild horses call it home. A handful of people live there year round. More if you count the ghosts.

Darkness fell and Captain Torrens and his men were on opposite ends of the island. The captain had been gone awhile but it was too late and stormy to head back. Luckily, he found a small hut that had been built years before to shelter the island's regular procession of stranded sailors, and he lit a small fire within it. He stepped outside, away from the hut for a moment, and then returned to an odd and troubling sight. His dog, who had remained in the hut, was now standing outside. His hair was raised and his teeth were bared. He stood facing the door to the hut and was barking and growling at something inside.

Already shaken by the day's tragic events, Captain Torrens steeled his nerve, pushed open the creaky door and peered inside.

There was a woman sitting by the fire. She was very pale and her long hair was dripping wet. So were her clothes. And she was covered in sand from head to toe. She looked like she had been spat out of the ocean and had dragged her fragile body across the beach to the hut.

"Good heavens, madam!" Captain Torrens gasped. "Who are you and where did you come from?"

The woman didn't answer either question. She slowly turned her head and fixed her watery eyes on the captain, then raised a shaking hand in the air. In the flickering light of the fire, the captain saw a grisly sight. The woman's ring finger had been crudely hacked off. The gory stump squirted blood that ran down her hand and forearm.

Assuming she was a survivor from the *Francis*, Torrens grabbed a bandage from an emergency kit he'd found, but the woman stood suddenly and walked out the door. When he followed her she moved faster. When the captain picked up his pace the woman began to run. Fearing she might be suffering from shock, Torrens ran as fast as she did. She ran all the way to the centre of the island, into a small lake . . . and then vanished from sight.

That was when Torrens realized he had seen a ghost. She confirmed this suspicion when she reappeared in the

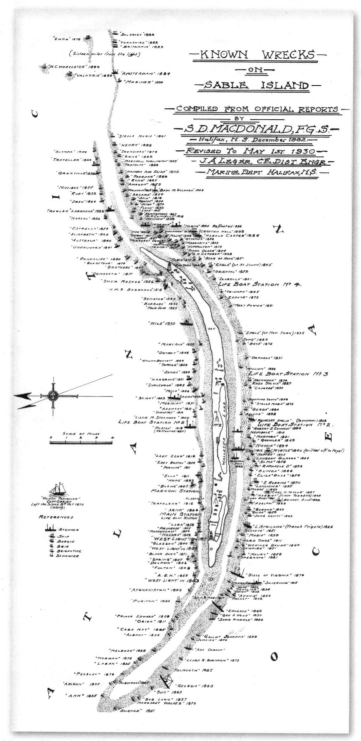

Map of Sable Island showing known shipwrecks since 1583

same hut the following night. As before, she spoke not a word and held up her bloody hand in the firelight.

That night, recognition suddenly struck the captain. He'd seen the woman before. She was the wife of Dr. Copeland, a medical officer who had commanded the *Francis* and was among the casualties on Sable Island.

"Is that you, Mrs. Copeland?" Torrens asked, sure it was her, but still having a hard time believing it.

The ghost nodded.

Torrens began to connect the dots and made an assumption. "You have been murdered for your ring?"

Again the ghost nodded.

She stood then, and backed out of the hut to disappear into the night once more. Over the years others have spotted her wandering up and down Sable Island after nightfall, always soaked to the bone and covered in sand. She forever prowls in the moonlight, searching for her missing ring and finger. It's possible she regularly walks past the island's other infamous ghost.

During the late 1800s, a twelve-man crew was tasked with rowing to Sable Island whenever there was a shipwreck. However, their rowboat was regularly joined by a mysterious thirteenth man. The man walked out of a cloud of island fog and into the shallow part of the ocean as the boat approached. He then boarded the rowboat without a word, picked up a spare oar and helped the crew row the rest of the way. And as they departed the island, the mysterious man would help row for a short distance before hopping out and floating back to the island, where he remained until the lifeboat returned. His silence was creepy enough, but worse was the bloody gash on his right cheek, revealing the man's teeth even when his mouth was closed. The skin around the wound was angry, red and oozed puss. And his facial wound never healed, not even during the long months between visits to the island.

In September 1899, one of the lighthouses on Sable Island burned to the ground during a big storm. The men tasked with cleaning up the charred debris made an unsettling discovery. A spade struck something hard that had been buried in the sand. It was a metal box. When the men pried it open they found a weathered lighthouse log inside it.

Flipping through the pages, a particular passage jumped out.

September 10th, 1856. Stormy. Wind blowing S. E. No vessels spoken. Howard Murray is dead. He died at ten o'clock this morning. The gash in his right cheek festered and blood poisoning set in. Before he died he said he would come back; that he would always go out with the lifeboat in which he had rowed stroke oarsman for many years. I wonder if he will. We buried him this afternoon on the point.

Chances are, with so many shipwrecks over the years and such a high death toll, the point where Howard Murray was buried was likely incredibly crowded. An island doesn't earn the name Graveyard of the Atlantic for nothing. It's little wonder that one or two of the people who have died there haven't remained beneath the sand.

HAUNTED HOUSE FOR SALE

Kelowna, British Columbia

Ten years is a long time — longer still if the months, weeks, days and hours are filled with unexplained sounds, doors opening on their own and physical altercations with unseen attackers. But a single mother lived with her son in their Kelowna home for a decade before finally deciding they had dwelled long enough with the spirits she called "The Others."

After she purchased the house, The Others wasted no time making their presence known. The first incident happened before she and her son had even moved in. He was painting the house late one night with a friend, while the mother was at their old home packing. After working for a few hours, the teens took a break. They sat on the floor in the middle of the living room and passed a few minutes in conversation. Suddenly the quiet of the empty house was interrupted. In the kitchen, cupboards flew open and then slammed shut with a bang loud enough to wake the dead. Startled, the boys yelled and jumped to their feet. And then the lights throughout the entire house started flashing on and off rapidly. The teens ran out the front door and down the street. The son only looked back once. Much to his dismay, the lights were still flashing.

When they made it safely back to his old house, short of breath and covered in a cold sweat, the son told his mother what had happened. He vowed that there was no way he was going to move into a haunted house.

"Don't be silly," his mother said with a roll of her eyes. "There's no such thing as ghosts." She was a no-nonsense kind of person who thought that anyone who did believe in ghosts was not only mistaken, but "nutty."

Her opinion would soon change.

She was sound asleep in her bedroom, exhausted from the move. Nothing unusual had happened since her son and his friend had abandoned their late-night painting. The night was quiet and dark. Suddenly, she was awakened by an awful commotion. It sounded like someone was crawling through the walls and banging on the pipes with a hammer. The sound slowly faded away, and with a little effort the woman drifted back to sleep.

But the midnight disturbance happened again the next four nights in a row. On the fifth night she snapped. She sat up in bed and shouted, "Please stop that noise right now!"

Amazingly, silence followed. She hadn't expected the

command to have any effect. She waited as the seconds ticked by, expecting the banging on the pipes to resume, but it didn't.

"Thank you," she said in shock. She then pulled the covers over her head and hid until the sun rose the next morning. Nothing ever banged on the pipes again, but it wasn't the last time the presence made itself heard.

The woman's son had friends spending the night and they were hanging out in the basement. Late at night the woman heard more banging, this time coming from below her room. She knew it wasn't the pipes, but she couldn't figure out what it was. After five minutes of uninterrupted commotion, she yelled downstairs and told the boys to cut it out and go to sleep.

"We're not doing anything," her son called up with a tremble in his voice. "We're not making that noise."

The woman ran down the stairs and found the three boys huddled on the couch. They were shaking, and their faces looked petrified. They were staring with wide eyes at the door to the basement bedroom. It was closed. The banging was coming from within. The mother threw the door open. The banging abruptly stopped. There was no one inside the room.

Without knowing anything about the previous owners and the house's history, it was difficult to figure out why their house would be haunted. But the woman soon made a startling discovery that confirmed the house was a hotbed of paranormal activity, and whoever lived there before them must have known it too.

The discovery came when mother and son were

organizing items to be stored away. Their new house had a cupboard under the basement stairs. After setting down a load of boxes, the mother and son opened the door and peered inside. She waved a flashlight around in the dark, cramped space, illuminating dust, strands of tangled spiderwebs and crayon drawings and letters on the risers of the steps. They couldn't decipher the meaning of the markings but thought it was an unusual place for a child to play.

Shrugging off the odd discovery, the son handed boxes to his mother, who stacked them neatly under the stairs. That's when she noticed that the cupboard wasn't empty. There was something shoved deep into a dark crevice. Whether the previous owner forgot it or left it behind on purpose will never be known. But the mother instantly regretted finding it. It was a Ouija board.

This was no store-bought Ouija board; it was home-made. The board was constructed of wood, and the words, letters and numbers had been imprinted into its face using a wood-burning tool. The planchette, the tool spirits use to point at the letters and numbers on the board in order to communicate with the living, was made of marble.

But the board wasn't in perfect condition. There was a circle burned in its centre and it was cracked in half. It looked like some sort of evil energy had destroyed it.

The mother quickly shoved the homemade Ouija board and planchette into a plastic bag and took it to the curb to be picked up the next garbage day. She didn't care what happened to it or where it ended up, so long as it wasn't in her house for another second. But as time passed and the

21

creepy occurrences continued, she began to wonder if she had done the right thing or made a terrible mistake.

She later learned that if a Ouija board has been opened in order to reach out to the dead, it needs to be closed when the conversation is over — by pointing the planchette at the bottom of the board where it says GOOD BYE — in order to stop unwanted spirits from entering our world at will. She grew fearful that she had unwittingly left a portal to some other dimension wide open.

The disturbances in her house grew more frequent, varied and terrifying. One afternoon, she was taking a nap on the couch when her son quietly walked past her to the kitchen. He froze as soon as he entered the kitchen and called back to his dozing mother: "You need to see this."

She walked in, rubbing sleep out of her eyes. All of the kitchen cupboards had been opened forty-five degrees, and each of the drawers had been opened a hand span.

At Christmastime, the family's tree was also meddled with. The morning after they put up and decorated the tree, the son awoke to find all the decorations on the floor. None were broken, ruling out the possibility that they had all fallen — however unlikely that would have been. Furthermore, each of the ornament hooks had been straightened. He diligently bent back each of the hooks and rehung the decorations. When he had finished the monotonous task, he decided that he would try to reason with the ghost that had targeted the tree.

"If you absolutely have to play with the tree," he said to the empty room, "one, maybe two ornaments are acceptable, but that's it. No more."

There were two ornaments on the floor beside the tree the next morning. Their hooks had been straightened. This happened every day until Christmas.

Some time later, as the woman was watching television, she saw something moving out of the corner of her eye. Materializing through the floor immediately to her right was a dark grey cloud of smoke that she described as spongy and semi-transparent. She blinked and rubbed her eyes in disbelief. When she looked again the smoke was still there. The grey mass rose into the air and floated a metre or two away from her before it vanished.

Night was a particularly threatening time and it was virtually impossible to get any rest, let alone peace. One evening, as the mother was settling into her recliner for a nap, she closed her eyes and immediately felt someone press down on her mouth. Her eyes shot open, but there was no one else in the room. Another time, after slipping beneath her bedsheets, invisible fingers stroked her hair just above her forehead. The scariest encounter was when she rolled over in bed in the middle of the night and something grabbed her neck and squeezed. She broke free from whatever was gripping her and yelled in a firm voice, "Don't ever touch me like that again!" Fortunately, that was the last time it ever happened.

There were countless other unexplained events and disturbances that the mother and son had to live through during their time in the house. But after ten years of living with the dead, it was time for them to move on. So they set out to sell the house in an unusual fashion, posting the following description online:

"Haunted House" For Sale

In the market for a "real" haunted house? Looking for a house with a ghostly presence? Look no further! I have the house for you . . . ghosts included!

The house certainly has a lot of character — and some of it lives in the walls.

HUNTED

Stony Rapids, Saskatchewan

Claude Arteaux raced through the woods. As a young huntsman and fisherman who spent most of his time in the bush, he wasn't accustomed to the ice-cold fear that pumped through his veins. His heart hammered and sweat poured off his brow as he dodged trees and jumped over roots. The cool autumn air burned his lungs as he sucked in gasp after gasp. Claude didn't hear the gentle rustle of the wind blowing through trees, the steady hum and flow of running water, nor the crunch of the red and yellow leaves beneath his feet. As he ran, the only sound playing in his mind — over and over like a demonic recording on an endless loop — was the half wail, half shriek of the wraith he and the other hunters had heard far off in the woods nearly an hour before.

It was the fall of 1939 and Claude's father was leading a hunting and fishing expedition along Porcupine River, also known as Dead Man's River to the Dene people, near the Arteauxs' hometown of Stony Rapids. It was a wild, dangerous land at the northern border of Saskatchewan, but the Arteauxs weren't easily spooked. As men of the woods, they had seen their fair share of wild creatures and encountered many life-risking situations over the years, and they had always come out on top. But the shriek they had heard that day was unlike anything they had ever heard before. It didn't sound like a human or like an animal. It sounded like . . .

It sounded like the river wraith, Claude thought. But he quickly put that out of his mind. The river wraith wasn't real. It was simply a legend the townsfolk liked to tell to scare children and tourists.

His father had asked Claude to remain with their group, and then set off to try to find what had made the inhuman sound. Claude wanted to accompany his father, but he also knew someone had to remain with the inexperienced men, so he'd agreed to his father's request.

With every second that ticked by, the men grew more nervous, and the knot in Claude's stomach grew tighter. He began to imagine countless tragedies and horrors that could have befallen his father, each one more gruesome than the last.

Finally, when his nerves had stretched to their breaking point, Claude looked at the ashen faces of the men and said, "I'd best go take a look." Without giving them time to protest or talk him out of leaving them, Claude set off into the woods, following the northern path his father had taken. He ran through the bush and burst out of the thick cover on the bank of the Porcupine River. He crept half a kilometre along the river with his rifle at the ready, desperately searching for any sign of his father. Finally, he found him.

Claude's father was standing at the water's edge, his arms dangling limply at his sides and his rifle in the mud beside his feet. He was staring, transfixed, at something floating in the air above the river.

Claude couldn't believe his eyes. It was a phantom-like cloud of mist in human form. The apparition pulsed as if it had a beating heart and blood pumping through its veins.

"Dad!" Claude shouted.

His father didn't budge.

"DAD!" Claude yelled, even louder than before.

At this his father ripped his eyes off the ghost and spun to face his son. He raised his hand in panic. "Don't come any closer! Turn your back and don't look around!"

Not only did Claude stop moving as his father had warned, but he stopped breathing for a long time too. His father rushed to his side and said, "Let's get out of here right away. I've just seen the lost river wraith, and you know what that means."

All too well, Claude thought. It was believed that, many years before, a murderer had been chased out of Stony Rapids by an angry mob of citizens. The vigilantes shot the murderer in the back then dragged him kicking and screaming into the river. They held him beneath the surface of the water and dropped a large boulder on his legs,

27

crushing his kneecaps and pinning him underwater. He drowned. The dead man's spirit haunted that particular part of the river from that day forward, and it was believed that anyone who ventured too close to the ghost — whether by accident or on purpose — would die within a year.

Three months later, at the age of fifty-two and in excellent physical shape, Claude's father died. His last words to his son were, "You know where the wraith is. Don't ever go near that place on the river again."

Even once the soul-crushing loss of his father began to fade, Claude would not return to that cursed spot. Curiosity seekers begged him to lead them to it, but he flatly refused. His pain was still too raw, his fear too real.

One of Claude's old friends, a young man by the name of Roger Leclaire, didn't believe Claude's story, at least not the part about the misty wraith hanging above the river. And Roger certainly didn't believe that anyone who saw it would die soon after.

"One day," Roger was fond of saying, usually accompanied by a dismissive laugh, "I will go looking for your 'river wraith.'" No one took Roger seriously when he said this, but one day he did indeed set off on a trip up and down the Porcupine River in search of the ghost.

He didn't return. Well, not alive. His waterlogged corpse was dragged out of the river and returned to Stony Rapids. It was reported by the men who discovered Roger's body that the dead man's face was frozen in a look of blind terror.

For as long as he was able, Claude continued to lead hunting and fishing expeditions in the woods of northern

Saskatchewan, but he stayed true to his promise to his father and never returned to the river wraith's location. For as talented and skilled a hunter as Claude was, he was no match for the ghost who hunts men to their deaths.

WHEN DREAMS BECOME NIGHTMARES

Whitehorse, Yukon

When eight-year-old Keely Osland's family moved out of their mobile home and into a four-bedroom house in the Riverdale neighbourhood of Whitehorse, everything seemed too good to be true. Keely and her older brother, Nolan, each had their own room, and there was very little they wanted that they lacked. Riverdale, which is surrounded by three large mountains and the Yukon River, is situated in a beautiful part of the country with plenty of wilderness for adventurous young children to explore. The Osland siblings felt like they were living a dream come true, but the dream was about to become a nightmare.

It would be the family's pets that first noticed that something about the house wasn't quite right. The older of their two cats, Puss, was a lazy animal who did nothing but lie around all day. But once they moved into the house in Riverdale, something upset him and he began to act very strangely. At seemingly random times throughout the day and night, Puss would jump in the air and race up and down the stairs. And the younger cat, Chucky, who Keely described as being too fat to get up when they put out his food, often raced up and down the stairs as if possessed. It made Keely and her family feel very uncomfortable. It was as if the cats could sense something the humans could not.

Two years after she moved in, Keely and her nine-year-old cousin, Lindsay, not only sensed, but saw, what had spooked Puss and Chucky. It was a cold winter night in January and the two girls were alone in the basement. It was late when they were playing with a Barbie dollhouse and some baby dolls Lindsay had received for Christmas. The girls were tired but having fun, when suddenly two of the dolls' bottles levitated above the ground and floated in mid-air. The girls stared at the floating toy bottles in transfixed horror. The bottles danced left to right and right to left in perfect unison. And then, as abruptly as they had risen off the carpet, they dropped to the floor. The girls screamed and ran up the stairs, leaving the creepy doll toys behind.

The bottles weren't the only objects that defied gravity in the basement of Keely's house. Window blinds often shot up on their own. And a few days after the bottle incident, a blanket lifted off the floor into the air, lingered for a few seconds, then dropped back down. Eventually Keely refused to go down to the basement by herself.

One day, another young cousin named Ian was sleeping over and was in the Riverdale house alone. He made sure all the doors were locked and then settled on the couch in the upstairs family room to watch a television show. Unexpectedly, the back door on the main floor slammed shut. Ian was sure he had checked it on his rounds, and he hadn't even heard it open before it closed.

Summoning all his courage, he rose from the couch and crept through the hall and down the stairs. No one else was in the house — so far so good. But Ian made an unsettling discovery when he reached the back door. It was still locked. Confused and not wanting to give the matter any further thought, he returned to the family room and tried to get back into his television show.

But Ian wasn't going to watch any more TV that evening. Shortly after he sat back down on the couch, he heard another sound. Not a door slamming — something worse. The sound of heavy footsteps coming toward him — up the stairs and down the hall, closer, closer, closer . . .

Fortunately Keely's family returned at that exact moment, and the phantom footsteps stopped immediately. Ian rushed to meet the family, terror and relief fighting for dominance of his facial expression.

The Oslands moved to a new house some years later and their cats returned to their old habits. Puss spent more time dozing in sunbeams, while Chucky regained the weight he'd lost in Riverdale. Neither raced up and down the stairs ever again.

IN A DARK, DARK FOREST

Pontiac, Quebec

It was a cold winter made colder still by the unearthly intruder who made nightly visits to the Gillies Company lumber camp in Pontiac, Quebec.

Late at night, when the only sounds were the snores of the lumberjacks in their cabins and the soft fall of a gentle snow in the deep woods, a mystery woman would suddenly appear. She often lurked behind the stables. The teamsters — the men who took care of the animals necessary to the camp's daily operations — were the ones who regularly saw her. She was young and beautiful but her face was etched with sorrow. She seemed shy and easily spooked, and she disappeared when approached, but she continued to materialize each and every day after nightfall.

"What the Devil do you want here?" one teamster finally

blurted out one night when the moon was at the highest point in the sky.

Much to his surprise, the woman replied.

"I am John Sloan's wife," the ghost said with a voice as soft as freshly fallen snow. "When I died, John took my wedding ring off my finger. I want it back."

John was the bush foreman and well liked and respected around camp. Word of the encounter spread through

Lumber baron John Gillies

camp, and soon everyone knew that his wife was haunting the woods around them. Hopeful that John might dispel the ghost's claim and thereby provide a little comfort or relief, the men asked if he had indeed taken his wife's ring. When he confirmed that he had taken the ring before he buried her in their hometown of Vinton just a few weeks before, panic seized the camp. Now that he had corroborated the story, the men knew that the ghost was real, and they were fearful that she would become agitated, possibly aggressive, if she didn't get what she wanted.

That was enough to tempt all the lumberjacks and other workers to jump camp. Lumber baron John Gillies knew he had a big problem brewing. If all of his men, or even a fraction of them, suddenly left without replacements, he would stand to lose a fortune.

Gillies went to John Sloan and gave the foreman an order, the likes of which he never could have imagined he'd have to give. "You had better lay this ghost to rest," he told John with dead seriousness, "or we'll all be out of work here."

John agreed. He returned home to Vinton and told his extended family what had happened back at camp. The Sloans were a large clan who were opinionated and strong willed. When they heard John's plan to have his wife's body exhumed, they took up two sides on the matter. Half of the family were morally opposed to the idea; to dig up a body that had already been laid to rest was against their religion. Bad things would happen if this course of action was followed, and they could not consent to it. The other half felt worse calamities would befall the men in the lumber camp if John's wife's ghost was denied, sacrilege or no sacrilege. To do nothing, they cautioned, would only serve to enrage an undead spirit who could find no peace without her ring.

Tempers flared and the two sides nearly came to blows over the disagreement, but John was a man of his word and he had come to do a job. Without the assistance or blessing of half his family, he exhumed his wife's body, slipped the ring onto her bony, decomposing finger and returned to the lumber camp.

That night, just as the teamsters were beginning to believe the plan had worked and they were rid of the ghost, she appeared once again behind the stables. A quiet moment passed as she looked at the men and they looked at her. And then with a slight smile and a nod, the ghost held up her left hand for all to see. Her golden wedding band shone brightly in the moonlight.

She disappeared and was never seen in the Gillies lumber camp again — nor anywhere else on this earthly plane.

THE BEDROOM IN THE BASEMENT

Calgary, Alberta

For many teenagers, the day they are finally allowed to move into a basement bedroom is a proud one. It's a sign of respect from parents who now feel their child is mature enough to be separated by a floor or two at night. The freedom and independence that comes with sleeping in the basement is a dream come true.

For sixteen-year-old Rick Goodwin, moving into the basement of his family's new home was more of a *nightmare*.

The teen immediately called dibs on the basement room when he and his mother moved into the duplex on Beaver Dam Way in 1992. His mother, Barbara, didn't put up a fight. He was a responsible boy, and she and her two younger children would sleep in the three upstairs bed-rooms. Everyone was happy, but the happiness would only last for two weeks.

On September 19, fourteen days after they moved in, Barbara heard the loudest banging imaginable coming from the basement. She had been unpacking some boxes that had been neglected since moving into the new home. She looked at the clock. It was 11:55 p.m. Why was Rick making such a commotion so late at night? It sounded like he was pounding nails into the wall studs. The racket was so loud that Barbara was afraid it would wake the other children, and maybe even their neighbours. She marched down the stairs as her temperature started to rise.

Bang! Bang! Bang! The noise got louder and louder as she made her way into the basement. Barbara realized the sound was too loud to be caused by a hammer, and she still couldn't figure out what her son was doing. But just as she reached the bottom step, the noise suddenly stopped. She waited, listening in the dark, half-expecting the sound to start up again. It didn't, so she decided to head back upstairs without bothering Rick. He'd probably got it in his head to hang a picture up on the wall. Now that he had finished doing whatever it was he was doing, Barbara just wanted to finish her own work.

As she walked up the stairs, she hugged her arms to her chest and tried to rub some warmth into them. The temperature had suddenly plummeted. She checked the thermostat on the main floor, which was set to a warm temperature. It must have been malfunctioning. The air was icy cold.

Bang! Bang! Bang!

Barbara jumped. She didn't know how it was possible, but the sound was even louder than before. She marched straight back down into the basement, furious that Rick could be so inconsiderate. She was playing out what she would say to him when she landed on the final step and the sound immediately stopped again. This time, Rick's door flew open and the startled boy ran out of the room.

"Mom!" he yelled, his eyes wild. "Did you hear that banging?"

The sound had come from his door, as if something was trying to bash its way in. Rick's cat stared at the door and shook in terror. The cat, who had spent nearly every night sleeping on Rick's bed, refused to enter his room from that day forward.

This was the beginning of a string of terrifying and unexplained activity that plagued the Goodwins over the coming months.

Just before midnight one night in September, Rick and his mother were together upstairs when they heard the banging on his bedroom door again. The racket occurred three separate times that night, but when Rick crept downstairs to go to sleep there was no sign that anything had been in his room.

At two in the morning on October 2, Barbara woke up to a very peculiar sound coming from the basement. Not the banging on her son's door, but the screeching of windows sliding back and forth. She went to the basement and confirmed that the windows were open, which was confounding. The windows had been covered in dirt and old cobwebs and had clearly not been opened in many years. As a result, they were practically locked shut with age, and Barbara had planned on loosening them sometime soon.

As three o'clock approached on October 14, a new sound woke Barbara. She slipped out of bed and wearily stumbled into the living room toward the source of the sound. She found it. In the middle of the floor was a small toy piano, playing a tune that echoed off the walls. Barbara stared at the electric toy in mute horror. She knew there were no batteries in that piano.

At midnight on November 2, Barbara heard a sound coming from Rick's bedroom. *Tap, tap, tap, tap.* She was in the dining room, directly above his room, and she happened to glance quickly out the window at the backyard. Something had triggered the motion-activated light, but there was no one back there. Then the back gate slowly swung shut on its own, as if someone had just passed through, but she hadn't seen a soul.

So far, each of these unexplained events had taken place in the middle of the night, but that soon changed. At noon on November 12, Barbara heard footsteps in the hall near the back door, then a muffled voice upstairs. There was no one in the hall, so she followed the sound of the voice. Bizarrely, the sound was coming from a dresser in one of the bedrooms. She opened a drawer and found a toy phone. From it came a hollow, soulless voice repeating the same message over and over and over.

Have a nice day!
Have a nice day!
Have a nice day!

Like the toy piano, the phone had no batteries.

Throughout the second half of November and the entire month of December, odd events continued to stack up on one another like caskets in an overcrowded cemetery. The doorbell rang repeatedly when no one was anywhere near the door. Footsteps pounded up and down the basement stairs. Odd smells with no discernible source filled the house. Locks unlocked themselves and doors swung open and closed. And then the ceiling in Rick's room began to disintegrate as if by water damage. Bits of wet plaster rained down on his bed, but a building contractor couldn't find the cause.

Shortly before New Year's Eve, Barbara sat down at the kitchen table and closed her eyes. The nearly constant presence that seemed to terrorize her and her family was driving her mad, and she felt like she was at the end of her rope. Not knowing what else to do, she asked aloud for some sign of the ghost's existence. She hoped to learn something — anything — that would help her deal with the ghost that dwelled in her home. Instead, what she found was a pair of handcrafted earrings she had lost shortly after moving into the house. They had appeared in the middle of the table where she sat.

Rick moved out of the basement. He couldn't bear the thought of spending one more night down below, alone but not alone. Interestingly, the paranormal activity slowed down from that day forward. It didn't go away completely, but the Goodwins were thankful for any small improvement. Whether the ghost had provided Barbara with her missing earrings as a peace offering or a show of its power is unknown.

THE MURDERED MAN

Ganges, British Columbia

Late at night, when all the customers have left and staff have locked the doors, the pub in the Harbour House Hotel truly comes to life.

In the darkened, silent room, the pinball machine turns on. The ball shooter pulls back and releases, sending the metal ball up the lane, out the chute and into the playfield. The ball bounces left and right, up and down, while the lights flash and sound effects blare. And when the ball finally passes the slingshots and approaches the out hole, the flippers knock it back up. These after-hours games have been known to last up to thirty minutes.

After the final ball has been played and the game is over, the jukebox turns on and the pages flip over until the perfect song is selected to suit the evening's mood. That

Harbour House Hotel

the jukebox is often unplugged at closing time doesn't stop it from playing.

Next up is the pub's television, which turns on with its volume blasting as loud as possible. That makes sense; it has to be cranked up to be heard over the music.

Finally, the staff calculator turns on and begins making random calculations. That isn't too surprising, since the Harbour House Hotel's resident ghost not only worked there but used to own the place.

Walter Herzog purchased the hotel, located in the sleepy town of Ganges on Salt Spring Island, in 1971 and immediately began putting his plans for the property into action. He added a new wing to the existing building in the hopes of transforming it into a grand resort that would attract customers from far and wide. Walter hit a major speed bump when, in 1972, the hotel burned down. Not to be dissuaded, he immediately began rebuilding it. The hotel was set to reopen in 1973, but a far greater tragedy was waiting around the corner.

On September 15, 1973, just days before the scheduled grand reopening ceremony, a burglar broke into the hotel and burst into Walter's private suite by burning the door. The owner was startled awake and sprang into action to defend his hotel. There was a struggle. Walter's body was found early the next morning by hotel staff. He had been shot five times in the chest and stomach and died in his room.

That very room was later turned into the hotel's pub, the site of the majority of the Harbour House's paranormal activity. Hotel manager Ann Ringheim feels like Walter's ghost is looking after his property and its staff. But not everyone is as comfortable with his spectral presence.

Musicians who perform in the pub can stay in the room directly beneath Walter's old suite free of charge, but even the allure of a complimentary night in a beautiful hotel isn't always enough to make them stay. Many have fled in the middle of the night despite being exhausted from their show. The unexplained sounds of the pinball machine, a sweeping broom, hushed conversations and a commotion that sounds oddly similar to that of a large body being dragged across the floor above make it nearly impossible to sleep.

Upon hearing that Walter's ghost haunts the hotel, Alexei Rainier, a psychic from White Rock, offered to exorcise the spirit to bring him peace. Ann likes having Walter's spirit around, so she declined the offer. But Alexei

Thompson Nicola Regional District Library System

Gulf Islands Driftwood

Serving the islands that make Beautiful British Columbia Beautiful

Fourteenth Year, No. 37   GANGES, British Columbia   Thursday, September 20, 1973 $4.00 per year in Canada , 10¢ copy

Ganges Home Is Damaged
Fire Takes Over At Dump

— FIREMEN ARE BUSY AS WOODS ARE DRY

Closure of the woods to industry left the garbage dump on Salt Spring Island without fire. For the past several weeks the garbage dumped at the site by Wally Twa has been left.

On Saturday the garbage took matters into its own hands and about 50 tons of rubbish broke out in flames.

Volunteer firemen went out to the dump and cut it back, but they expected it to burn for several days.

With the woods tinder-dry and bush ready to flare up at the drop of a match, the firemen were on the alert at the week end.

Saturday fire caused extensive damage to the home of Martin Christiansen, Park Drive By-passer reported that there was an explosion and the owner came out from the basement as a plume of smoke rose behind him.

The roof was already moving when the firemen arrived to put the fire out. Home is only three years old.

Firemen could offer no estimate of the extent of the damage which was extensive.

On Sunday a campfire at Mount Maxwell set fire to the brush around after being scattered but not fully extinguished Firemen put out the fire and damped down the ground.

EARL WESTWOOD VISITOR TO SALT SPRING ISLAND

Earl Westwood was back last week end. Mr. Westwood came to visit Salt Spring Island after a long absence. He was at one time member for Nanaimo and the Islands in the provincial legislature and held the portfolio of recreation and conservation in the Bennett government.

In the meantime he has been for many years British Columbia's Agent-General in London, Eng.

WALTER HERZOG VICTIM

HOTELIER IS SHOT DEAD

— GANGES MAN IS CHARGED

Walter Herzog, proprietor of Harbour House Hotel was shot to death in his suite at the hotel in the early hours of Saturday morning. He was found at about 2.30 on Saturday morning dead from five bullets in the chest and stomach.

Sound of the shots failed to penetrate the brick walls of the building and to alert residents or cleaning staff.

Door of the apartment had been burned and a gas can was found outside the building. It was surmised that entrance had been gained by burning the door. The room showed signs of a struggle.

It is reported that a sum of money was missing from the apartment and robbery is considered to be the motive for the killing.

Hotel employee Gary Kopp went to the owner's room on Saturday morning and reported the killing. On Saturday ferry travellers were delayed as every car leaving the island was searched by police for the murder weapon, a revolver.

Three men were taken by police for questioning on Saturday and later two of them were released. Walter Herzog, Port Coquitlam contractor, acquired the hotel in 1971 from the company in which the founding family of Crofton still held an interest. It was the apple of his eye and he planned to make it a resort to be famed up and down the coast, he told islanders at that time.

He went ahead and employed his own contracting company to construct the new wing at the east end of the site. It was then opened two years ago, with a new beer parlour and cocktail lounge as well as guest accommodation.

Last fall the main body of the hotel was burned to the ground when firemen saved the new wing from damage. The owner was uncertain for a time whether or to go ahead with reconstruction or to dispose of the building and business. He finally decided to go ahead and construction is almost finished. He was discussing tentative plans for a formal opening the day before his death.

During the past two years he has retained his residence at Port Coquitlam and has commuted to the island. He maintained a suite at the hotel for his own use during the time he was on the island and for an overflow suite at any time he might run short of accommodation in the future.

The deceased man had an impressive story. He came to Canada as an immigrant shortly after the Second world war. For a time he lived in Winnipeg and gained familiarity with the language as well as studying his chosen trade of plumber.

He worked for contractors before finally setting out himself to a successful career. The hotel was his dream project.

The hotelier planted an extensive visit to his native Russia when the hotel was completed and a manager had been installed.

He took an interest in the affairs of the community and

(Turn to Page Sixteen)

On Monday Norman Morris Stevens, 23, of Ganges, was formally charged with capital murder in Sidney Provincial Court. No plea was taken and he was remanded to Monday, Sept. 24. Stevens is an Island man and attended school here.

HOUSE GUTTED IN SATURDAY FIRE

GANGES SAILORS PREPARE

Sailors are a busy group on Salt Spring Island this week as sabot racers prepare for the national sabot championships.

The national contest will be staged in Ganges Harbour this week end. Events will start on Saturday and continue into Sunday, with finals in plenty of time for contestants to reach Long Harbour for the afternoon sailing of the Vancouver ferry.

HISTORIANS TO MEET AT MAYNE ISLAND SUNDAY AFTERNOON

A meeting of the Gulf Islands Branch of the B. C. Historical Association will be held on Mayne Island, on Sunday, Sept 23 at 1:30 pm at the Agricultural Hall, President Donald New will be in the chair. A short business meeting will precede a talk given by Jesse Brown on Rocky Mountain House, Alberta.

SPORT CLUB PLANS TO FIND OUT
Why Are There No Fish ?

Where have all the fish gone? Salt Spring Island Rod and Gun Club are taking a close look at the fishing scene and a special meeting will be held at the Rod and Gun Club hall on Scott Road on Wednesday evening, Oct. 3.

Spokesmen for the fisheries department will be on the island to help members to analyse the fishing pattern.

The speakers will be asked for the loss of fish. Scarcity has been attributed to overfishing, bottom fishing in winter months and to the opening

of the herring fishing in Ganges Harbour. Discussion will not be narrowed down to the Harbour.

Fishermen, sport or commercial should find the meeting interesting, said Fred Morris. He urged Salt Spring Islanders to make a point of attending in the hopes of coming up with a logical and workable answer.

Coming to the island will be the fisheries Officer from Duncan and a biologist from Vancouver.

Meeting will be open to the general public.

This was a modern, two-storey home on Park Drive in Ganges until fire ripped through the building on Saturday morning. It is the property of Martin Christianson, who suffered no injury but sustained an extensive loss.

Owner was at one time the janitor and gardener at the Court House in Ganges. Damage was partially covered by insurance.

Office Nears Finish

The North Salt Spring Waterworks District will move very soon to its new headquarters building located at Central on the Upper Ganges Road, east of the Highways Department yard.

The new building will provide indoor parking for work vehicles, a storage area for supplies and equipment and the general office. The land has been owned by the District for a number of years and used as an outdoor storage centre.

The move has been made necessary through the growth of the water system resulting in an increased work load for the staff and heavier administrative duties.

The building was constructed by Bangert Construction, under the supervision of a building committee consisting of Superintendent, Peter Cartwright, Trustee Jim Wilkinson, chairman of the committee and Trustee Norman Mouat.

L. I. P.

CHAMBER ASKS FOR IDEAS

Local Initiative Projects must be submitted to the federal government by mid-October.

Salt Spring Island Chamber of Commerce has launched a number of such projects in past years and is prepared to stay with it. On Thursday evening last week the Chamber decided to invite recommendations from the general membership and the public.

Projects must be geared to the employment of labour. The

labour may be skilled or unskilled and it will be paid for by the federal government in a continuing effort to combat winter unemployment. Materials are not found by the government.

Construction or similar project requiring quantities of materials will be approved if the community will find the materials.

In the past, LIP projects on the islands have included playground construction, footpaths,

woodland trails, renovation of Fulford Hall, construction of the sports grounds at Fulford and other projects aimed at improved community facilities.

Readers who have any ideas for such projects on Salt Spring Island should send them by mail to Box 111, Ganges, or call Driftwood.

Gulf Islands School District has already announced plans to launch a Local Initiatives Project.

The article in the top right gives an account of the killing of Walter Herzog.

claimed to have felt an overpowering surge of "turmoil and imbalance" when she entered the hotel and was concerned that Walter might begin to lash out, causing disturbances that would be terrifying and dangerous.

After hearing about Alexei's fears, Ann decided to check in on Walter. Late that night, standing alone in the pub, she looked around the empty room and asked Walter to send her a sign if he wanted to stay in the hotel.

The next morning, Ann discovered that the hotel's switchboard had gone off-line in the middle of the night without any apparent explanation. Three seemingly random numbers flashed on the display. When the numbers were matched to the corresponding letters on a telephone keypad, they spelled out a single short word: BOO.

It was, Ann reasoned, Walter's playful way to let her know that he has no interest in leaving the Harbour House Hotel anytime soon.

DEAD IN HER TRACKS

Conception Bay South, Newfoundland and Labrador

It was late fall and the evening air was cold. As the sun set on the small town of Conception Bay South, a sixteen-year-old boy walked home alone. He'd followed the train tracks home countless times before, always enjoying the peace and quiet of the woods. It was an opportunity to slow his pace, take extra-large breaths of crisp, fresh air and clear his mind. He'd heard the local folklore that surrounded the tracks, of course. But he'd never seen or heard anything unusual or unexplainable, so he wasn't afraid.

Very soon, he would have something to fear, and he'd never feel comfortable walking along the tracks again.

At first all the teenager heard were the soothing sounds

of rustling fall leaves and birds chirping in the treetops. But then he stopped walking. There had been another sound behind him, something he couldn't quite place. It had almost sounded like he was being followed.

He peered over his shoulder, back the way he had come. The sound stopped. There was no one there. His pulse quickened and he took a deep breath to calm his nerves, then told his imagination to stop trying to get the better of him. He shrugged his shoulders, put the thought out of his mind and carried on.

Before long he heard the footsteps behind him again. Now he was terrified but he found the courage to look back once more, despite the fact that every rational thought in his head was yelling at him to run away.

There was no one behind him — at least no one he could see — but he still heard the footsteps. They sounded to be about four and a half metres back, and they were getting steadily closer. The boy looked at the ground where he thought the sound was coming from. What he saw terrified him.

He still couldn't see whoever was approaching, but with every footfall he saw an indent in the crushed gravel in the exact shape of a foot. That was enough for the boy. He turned and ran in the opposite direction as quickly as his legs would carry him, praying that whatever had followed him on the tracks wouldn't follow him all the way home.

The legend of Conception Bay South claims that long ago a young bride-to-be named Miss Molloy was left standing at the altar when her groom got cold feet and skipped town. Distraught and depressed, she fled the church alone and wandered along the train tracks near Easons Road. Whether or not she found any peace there before tragedy struck, no one will ever know.

She heard the not-so-distant whistle of an approaching train, so she took a step off the tracks. But as she took her second step, her long, flowing wedding dress got caught on a railroad spike. The train barrelled around some trees. She froze momentarily like a deer in headlights as the train quickly closed the gap toward her. The gravity of the situation slammed into her and she broke out of her terrified trance. She pulled and yanked and struggled and screamed and cried, but she couldn't free her dress. The train shattered her body and carried on without slowing, as if she'd been nothing more than a loosely packed scare-crow accidentally forgotten on the tracks.

Ever since that day, the ghost of Miss Molloy has been heard walking up and down the old tracks late at night, forever searching for the groom who left her on their wedding day.

The ghost has not only been heard, but she's been seen too. Late one night not too long ago, a young woman named Natasha had enjoyed an evening out with friends and she was walking home along the tracks. Her mind was elsewhere when she looked up ahead and saw something that took her breath away. Suspended in mid-air was a patch of grey fog that somehow wasn't blown apart in the wind. Confused by the sight and overcome with curiosity, Natasha approached the odd shape and refused to take her eyes off it. As she got closer and closer, the fog slowly took the form of woman in a long white gown. The ghost bride's head was tilted down as if she was overcome by grief. But when Natasha was close enough to reach out and touch her, the spectral woman turned and floated off the tracks, onto a small path that led to the road. Natasha hurried to keep up, but when she turned onto the path a second later, the ghost was gone.

In Conception Bay South, there is no such thing as living on the right side or wrong side of the tracks. There's only the living side . . . and the dead side.

A SUMMER VACATION TO DIE FOR

Niagara-on-the-Lake, Ontario

Kyle was fourteen when she spent the summer in Niagara-on-the-Lake, considered to be one of Canada's most haunted cities, with her mother's best friend, Jeannette. Kyle had registered for sailing lessons, and Aunt Jeannette had kindly agreed to let the teen stay with her in her house. The beautiful old home sat on a street lined with mature trees. Built in 1818 by John MacMonigle, MacMonigle-Craik House was known to be the site of unusual disturbances and activity, but Kyle knew nothing of it. Aunt Jeannette certainly didn't warn her. So Kyle didn't anticipate that her summer vacation would be filled with anything but sun, fun and relaxation.

Had she known the truth, she might have packed a Ouija board and an EVP (electronic voice phenomena) tape recorder next to her flip-flops and sunscreen.

After her first day sailing, Kyle returned home in the middle of the afternoon with windblown hair and the beginning of a tan. Aunt Jeannette wasn't home, but she had given Kyle her own key. So the girl let herself into the house. Looking forward to changing into some fresh clothes and then settling down with a book and a cold drink, Kyle headed for her room. She tried to open the door, but it banged against something heavy and wouldn't open more than a crack. A large dresser appeared to have been dragged across the room and pushed up against the door. She decided to wait downstairs in the kitchen, wondering why Aunt Jeannette had barred entry to the room.

When Aunt Jeannette finally arrived a few hours later, Kyle explained what had happened. Aunt Jeannette went silent and her smile fell from her face. She didn't speak as she led the girl upstairs. Together they were able to push the door open enough for them to slip into the room and move the dresser back to its proper place against the wall.

Once the work was done, Aunt Jeannette finally broke her silence. "There is," she said faintly, after one or two false starts, "a poltergeist in this house."

Kyle couldn't believe what she was hearing. Even if her mother's friend was telling the truth, why hadn't she warned her?

Whether Aunt Jeannette was in denial or had hoped nothing would happen while Kyle stayed with her, Kyle never knew. The one thing she did grow to realize — rather quickly, and terrifyingly — was that Aunt Jeannette wasn't mistaken, confused or lying. There most certainly was a poltergeist inhabiting the house, and it was decidedly unfriendly.

The following day, after another enjoyable afternoon of sailing, Kyle returned to find the dresser blocking her door. Once again she couldn't move it on her own and needed to wait for Aunt Jeannette to return and help. Was a poltergeist definitely to blame? Or was it possible someone — a friend of Aunt Jeannette's, perhaps, or Aunt Jeannette herself — was playing a practical joke? But the dresser was so large and heavy that Kyle couldn't imagine how one person could move it alone. And then there was the fact that it would have been impossible to leave the room once the door was blocked, unless the perpetrator had jumped out the second-floor window. But that seemed unlikely too.

The door was blocked again on the third day. The fourth too. It happened every day for a few weeks. And there was never a sign that anyone else had been in the house or exited through the bedroom window. Kyle became convinced that there truly was a poltergeist in the house. And she came to believe the spirit didn't like her living there and wanted to make her summer as troublesome and frightening as possible.

Weird goings-on with the dresser weren't the only activities that Kyle and Aunt Jeannette attributed to the poltergeist. The household cat often stalked the ghost through the house even though no one else could see it. Window curtains had a habit of closing on their own, suddenly and loudly. And one night Aunt Jeannette was sitting at the kitchen table when five or six tomatoes rose off the counter and flew straight against the windowpane, smashing into a bloody pulp that splattered across the kitchen and ran down the glass.

Then, one day, Kyle finally had some good luck. She returned from sailing, walked upstairs, turned the doorknob to her room and was shocked when the door swung all the way open. She stood in the doorway for a full minute, eyes wide and jaw slack, staring at the dresser in disbelief. It was in its proper place against the wall.

She walked across the room in a daze and reached out to touch the dresser, half-convinced her eyes were playing

MacMonigle-Craik House

a trick on her. Her fingers touched wood — the dresser was real, and it was really in its usual spot. Kyle was about to leave when she noticed something wasn't quite right. Everything that was kept on top of the dresser — flowers, her hairbrush and a handful of small objects — had been removed. She found them a moment later on the other side of the room, placed in a perfectly straight line on the windowsill.

This happened again and again, day after day. It made no sense, but it successfully drove Kyle to the brink of insanity.

Many years have passed. It's safe to say that Kyle will never forget the summer vacation she spent in Niagara-on-the-Lake.

KELLOW'S HOLLOW

Cornwall, Prince Edward Island

On the outskirts of town there's a bridge. Under the bridge runs a small brook. And beside the brook stands a large pine tree. During the day, it's a peaceful setting ideal for summer picnics and naps in the shade. But after nightfall, Kellow's Hollow is a dark and ominous locale where sinister legends abound. See that bridge? Countless people have died there, the locals claim. Never venture near the brook under a full moon, they warn outsiders. And that pine tree? Well, a man once hanged himself from its branches, and that's not even the worst of it.

Cornwall was first settled in the mid-1700s as a farming community immediately west of Charlottetown, the provincial capital. It was in the town's early days that a local farmer, Jack Connaway, spent a cold November night by the stone fireplace in Noah's Ark, the village pub. He drank whisky, sang songs and told tall tales deep into the night. When the crowd began to disperse, Jack stepped outside but he barely felt the cold air's sting. He mounted his horse and spurred her toward home. Bed was beckoning, but his spirits were high and he felt nearly unstoppable. He didn't even slow down as he approached Kellow's Hollow, despite the fact that he knew full well that it was a cursed area best avoided at night.

His horse slowed down and seemed hesitant to cross the bridge, as if she possessed some sixth sense that urged her to turn around.

"Easy there, old girl. There's nothing to be afraid of," Jack whispered into her ear with a gentle pat on her neck. "Easy does it. Easy, old girl."

His soothing words and touch gave the horse enough courage to continue. But when they reached the centre of the bridge, a blood-curdling scream rose from the brook beneath them and shattered the night's silence. The horse reared up on her hind legs and sent Jack flying out of his saddle. He cracked his head on the railing as he plummeted over the bridge. He died before he hit the ground.

James Kellow was the only witness to the tragedy, but there was nothing he could do to save Jack. After Jack died that night in November, his spirit haunted the area along with other misty apparitions, all of whom were said to dwell within the large pine tree beside the brook.

A few months later, Jack's brother, Michael, neared Kellow's Hollow on horseback. He was overcome with grief as he approached the bridge, thinking that his brother had been taken from this world far too soon. The moon was round and full in a cloudless sky, casting a silvery-blue glow on the land.

Although he was hesitant to cross the bridge that had killed his brother, his destination lay on the other side of the brook and going around would be far too long a detour. He put his head down and rode forward, eager to cross as quickly as possible.

But once he reached the spot where his brother had died, Michael's horse came to an abrupt stop and began snorting and stamping her hooves. Before he could try to soothe her, Michael noticed that the pine tree was lit up with many lights of different colours and sizes. He rubbed his eyes in disbelief, but the lights remained when he looked again. Suddenly, the lights fell to the ground as if something had run straight into the tree and knocked them loose.

In the silence that followed, Michael heard the sound of an approaching horse. But when he turned to see who was there, he was startled to find the bridge was empty. Still, the phantom horse rode toward him. When the sound of hooves reached his own horse, Michael heard a whisper that materialized and floated straight out of thin air.

"Easy there, old girl. There's nothing to be afraid of," the disembodied voice said. "Easy does it. Easy, old girl."

There was no mistaking the voice. It belonged, Michael knew, to his late brother Jack.

"Jack?" Michael called out in shock.

As if summoned, Jack materialized at the side of the bridge, followed by nineteen other spectres, each glowing white. Michael was rendered speechless and became frozen with fright. He could neither call for help nor turn and flee as the ghosts solemnly drifted across the bridge. One by one, they entered the pine tree and disappeared. It was the final time Michael saw Jack, dead or alive. The living brother never returned to Kellow's Hollow.

The tree was later cut down and a church was built where it once stood, but reports of midnight wails, unusual light orbs and sickly looking spirits in Kellow's Hollow continue to trickle out of the brook.

GHOSTS ON DISPLAY

Lethbridge, Alberta

It was in the Galt Museum & Archives' basement that Mike Prokop encountered George Benjamin Bailey. Many others have also seen George in the old building. George, you see, lives there. Although, *lives* might not be the most accurate term. George *haunts* there.

Mike had been asked by the museum to help with a research project, and he was in the basement with Richard Shockley, the collection technician. They had noticed that there were some errors in one of their reports, so they went downstairs to make the corrections on the museum's computer. They were alone, but suddenly Mike stopped working and lifted his hands off the keyboard. With a frown, he turned to Richard and asked, "Did you hear that?"

Mike had heard footsteps approaching from behind.

And it had sounded like someone shuffling across the floor in socks, not shoes. He and Richard stood up and walked down the hall. It was empty.

As they approached the end of the corridor, the temperature began to plummet. And when they reached the elevator shaft, a blast of cold air rushed out and enveloped them, making their hair stand on end and covering their skin in goosebumps. It was not, Mike insists, the feeling of a blowing breeze. It was something not from this world, and it made him feel incredibly uncomfortable.

George has that effect on visitors and museum staff alike. He spends most of his time in the dark depths of the building, usually near the elevator. That's not surprising since that's where he met a most unfortunate fate.

It was 1933 and George was an admired farmer in the area. At that time, the Galt Museum was the Galt Hospital, and George checked in for an appendectomy, a routine and minor surgery. The operating room was on the second floor, so a hospital attendant wheeled George to the elevator on a gurney. His wife, Alice, walked beside him. The elevator door opened, and the attendant began to roll the gurney forward. But when George was only halfway in, the elevator lurched to life for no apparent reason and travelled up toward the second floor. Alice and the hospital attendant stood by helplessly and watched in horror as the gurney's legs got caught on the edge of the elevator. George and the gurney were both picked up into the air. Time seemed to slow down as George dangled below the elevator, but then he slipped off the gurney and plummeted headfirst to the bottom of the elevator shaft in the base-

Galt Museum

ment. Remarkably, George survived the fall. He was found wandering around the basement corridor in pain, in shock and in his bare feet. He succumbed to the head trauma a short time later and died.

Richard Shockley, the man who was working with Mike Prokop when they felt an icy blast of air whoosh out of the elevator, wasn't surprised by the paranormal experience. He'd already heard and seen George a couple of times before.

The first event occurred in the fall of 1985 when the building was being renovated. Richard was downstairs at his computer when he heard the same sound in the hall he would hear years later with Mike. Richard was overcome by the eerie sensation that he was no longer alone. After a short pause, the sound faded down the hall, back the way it had come.

The second occurrence was even more terrifying. He was working on his computer when the sound of shuffling feet approached his office. The sound stopped and began to recede, so Richard jumped up and raced into the hall. Through the windows of two locked doors he saw a soft white light float slowly and deliberately from one of the room's walls to the opposite one. He unlocked the doors and rushed inside, but the light was gone. All that remained was a cold, damp feeling in the air. Richard had felt a presence and was deeply unnerved. He knew that he had seen George's ghost.

But George isn't the only ghost that haunts the museum. A few others have been spotted in the building's upper floors, giving museumgoers a little extra bang for their buck — or the fright of their lives, depending on their point of view.

As a grade four class from a local school toured the museum on a field trip, a little boy named Jeff raised his hand and asked a question.

"Who's playing the nurse?" he said matter-of-factly.

The staff member leading the tour was puzzled. There was an old nurse's uniform on a mannequin in another part of the building, but there were no volunteers in period clothing in the museum. She explained that their group was alone. But Jeff insisted that he could see a nurse standing with her back to the group. And then the nurse, whom only Jeff could see, turned and stared straight at the young boy with deep, penetrating eyes.

It's believed the museum's second floor, which was once the Sunbeam ward for sick children, is the eternal resting place of children who were admitted to the hospital many years ago but never recovered. Museum educator Belinda Crowson has heard voices coming from a room on the second floor. Another employee looked back at the building as he left one day and saw the ghost of a little girl staring down at him from a second-floor window, waving goodbye. Others have seen two boys in the windows, watching the world age while they remain frozen in time.

George seems to enjoy the spectral company. True, he spends most of his time shuffling around the basement, but he's also fond of travelling up to visit the ghosts of the nurse and the children on the second floor. Although the elevator was replaced with a newer model a while back, it continues to travel up and down on its own with no living people inside it. One would think George would rather take the stairs than ride in the very contraption that took his life.

THE NIGHT TERRORS BEFORE CHRISTMAS

Liverpool, Nova Scotia

It was the night before Christmas and all through the house, not a creature was stirring . . .

But that was about to change.

A woman was settling into bed. It was late and she was exhausted after preparing for Christmas morning. Her husband was away on business, so all of the work had fallen to her. In the next room, the nursery, her baby was curled up in his crib. Her older children were asleep in their own rooms, no doubt with visions of sugar plums dancing in their heads. Suddenly the mother sat up in bed. She had heard a sound. The unmistakable creak of the closet door. She was certain the door had been firmly closed when she had lain down, but now it was wide open.

"No. Not tonight," the mother whispered in the darkness. "I am not doing this tonight so leave me alone." The family hadn't lived in the house for long, but their time there had been plagued by unexplained sounds, mysterious occurrences and terrifying encounters. She knew all too well that her house was haunted, and she couldn't bear the thought of facing the ghost without her husband, especially on Christmas Eve.

Whatever was lurking in the shadows of the closet listened to the mother and complied. The closet door swung shut with a click.

Desperately hoping that the spirit would remain in there, the mother settled back down and tried to fall asleep. It was no small feat, but as the minutes ticked by her eyelids grew heavy and her mind drifted, lulling her into a false sense of security.

In the nursery, the baby began to fuss, prematurely rousing the mother out of her slumber. She assumed he had awoken on his own and needed to be rocked back to sleep. She tried to sit up but found that she couldn't move a muscle. It was like she was paralyzed from the neck down, or worse, like someone was pinning her down to the bed.

As she struggled to move, she felt phantom knees dig into her shoulders, holding her prisoner in her own bedroom.

She started to panic. The baby was crying louder, more hysterically, and there was nothing she could do to help him. She herself needed help, and she needed it fast. She yelled as loudly as she could for her oldest son to wake up and help her. She would have preferred not to get him involved, but she was out of options and the situation was rapidly growing dire.

The boy woke with a start and jumped out of bed. He raced down the hall in a blind panic, thinking he might still be asleep and suffering from a horrible nightmare. Fortunately, when he reached his mother's room, the spirit that had pinned her down fled.

Now free, the mother ran to the nursery with her confused and scared son following close behind. The baby was standing in the crib and crying hoarsely, his face beet red with tears streaming down his cheeks. Thankfully, there were no ghosts in the room and the baby eventually calmed down in his mother's arms. But it took her a long time to get over the fright she had suffered, which cast a dark gloom over Christmas morning.

Their house's long and unique history might be to blame for the ghost that haunts its halls. Built in 1763, it was originally a bustling bar and inn named Dexter's Tavern that was conveniently located a stone's throw from a garrison, serving the soldiers who were stationed in town. And the town's port was a hub for Royal Navy ships, supplying a continuous stream of sailors looking for food, drinks and rooms to rent. It's believed that the ghost is a soldier of that era, but not an English spirit as one might expect. Some have claimed to see the ghost dressed in a French uniform and have heard him speaking to himself in French.

Although the building was constructed of local wood, the large and unique stones used for its foundation were likely transported from the ruins of the Fortress of Louisbourg, a French installation in Cape Breton that also happens to be haunted. Some Liverpool locals are insistent that the ghost of the French soldier came with the stones. After construction was complete, the ghost was left to wander Dexter's Tavern, forever wondering how he had become separated from his fellow soldiers. Perhaps this explains the anger he occasionally directs at the living.

As for the mother and her family who were accosted on Christmas Eve, they moved out after two short years that felt like an eternity. They were relieved to escape the ghost of Dexter's Tavern unscathed, and their subsequent Christmases have been blessedly merry, not scary.

Fortress of Louisbourg

THE HAUNTED HALL OF JUSTICE

Toronto, Ontario

In the mid-1960s, shortly after the last two hangings took place in Canada, odd things started happening in Toronto's Old City Hall. And the judges who held court in the building seemed to be the prime targets of the paranormal mischief.

Judge S. Tupper Bigelow regularly heard footsteps going up and down the stairs concealed behind a door beside the judge's bench. The stairwell leads from Courtroom 33 down to the street, giving judges private access to the courtroom, and up to the attic, which was empty at the time. No one else had any reason to use those stairs, yet Bigelow had definitely heard something and he was positive the sounds weren't the creaks and groans of an old building. They were footsteps, no doubt about it. He quietly opened the door and crept along the stairs in search of the person creating the racket, peering over his shoulder as he moved. No one was there. But then something grabbed hold of his judicial robes and yanked him violently.

Had this been an isolated incident, it might have been easier to brush aside. But Judge Peter Wilch experienced the exact same phenomenon. He heard phantom footsteps on the stairs, and then unseen hands clawed at his robe as if trying to pull him down the stairs to his death.

Both men felt that someone no longer living holds a grudge against the judicial system, a grudge that has outlasted the grave.

The most prevalent theory is that Ronald Turpin and Arthur Lucas haunt the Old City Hall in tandem. Turpin was convicted of killing a police officer, while Lucas was convicted of killing two witnesses who were part of a major drug case, and they were the last two men in the country to be hanged for their crimes. Their death sentences were announced in Courtroom 33. When Lucas's sentence was read, he calmly said, "Tough break." Although their crimes were unconnected, both Turpin and Lucas were executed on the same wintry day, December 11, 1962. The time? Two minutes after midnight. When told they would likely be the last two men ever hanged in Canada, Turpin responded dryly, "Some consolation." They were buried side by side in unmarked graves.

Many paranormal experiences have been reported, often late at night when Old City Hall is mostly empty . . . but far from quiet.

Jo Felquieras, a security guard, was walking alone

through an upper corridor. It was late: three o'clock in the morning. Suddenly a pair of unseen hands grabbed his ankles and held him in place as firmly as if his legs had been encased in cement. Despite being large and strong, he was unable to move for fifteen seconds until, finally, the hands released him and he ran out of the hall. But whatever spirit had held him in place might have followed him home. In the days that followed, he didn't feel like himself. He had trouble breathing and couldn't even talk. He sought the advice of doctors but no one could figure out what was wrong with him. Out of desperation, Felquieras went to a medium who told him he was possessed by an evil spirit and charged him $600 to exorcise it. A few short weeks before, he would have thought such a claim was a scam. Now he felt it was money well spent. He paid the fee, and after a two-week ordeal, the medium finally got rid of the spirit. Felquieras felt better immediately and was soon his old self again.

A maintenance worker, Joseph Bonett, hated working alone on Sundays. He'd spend long shifts in terror, listening to the sounds of many ghosts running back and forth on the floors above. He'd investigate but only discover what he knew to be true: the upper floors were all empty. And as soon as he got back to his desk, the sounds would start up again. It became so bad that Bonett eventually refused to leave his chair for his entire shift, whether his supervisor liked that or not.

Others have seen doors swing open on their own, objects get knocked off desks and a man dressed all in black standing atop the northwest tower, silently surveying the grounds below. Many employees have found the job too traumatizing, too scary, and have asked to be transferred. The manager of operations has granted the requests, no questions asked. Working in the haunted building is not for the faint of heart.

Nor is spending the night in Old City Hall, but that hasn't stopped many journalists from attempting the feat over the years. And what better night to sleep in an old, haunted building than Halloween? Although no one gets much shut-eye.

Agatha Bardoel, writing for the *Toronto Star*, and her sister, Frannie, thought they were up to the challenge. They rolled out their sleeping bags in the middle of the floor in Courtroom 33 and watched as the hands on the wall clock passed midnight. Looking for a bit of a thrill, they walked across the courtroom and sat down in the prisoner's box, the same box that had been briefly occupied by the men who'd been sentenced to hang years before. As soon as she sat down, Agatha felt unnaturally cold. The rest of the room was so hot she had needed to remove her sweater.

"I feel terrible," her sister said with a moan. "I don't understand it. I'm so anxious, like there's something awful that I've got to do, and I don't want to do it. And it's so cold . . ."

Frannie stood and faced the judge's bench at the front of the room, and immediately there was a loud *tap-tap-tap-tap* sound on the wooden floor beneath their feet. They quickly exited the box and slipped into their sleeping bags for comfort, warmth and security. They found the first two, but the third was not so easily attained.

"We shouldn't have done this," Frannie whispered.

But there was no turning back. Remembering that they had committed to this slightly mad plan to witness something precisely like what had happened in the prisoner's box, the sisters decided to get up and investigate another one of the allegedly haunted locations: the hidden stairwell beside the judge's bench.

They opened the door. The stairwell appeared to be empty, so they took a seat on the stairs and watched . . . and waited. It didn't take long before something odd began to happen.

"There's some kind of smoke through here," Frannie said.

Agatha watched with growing apprehension as the stairwell filled with mist that swirled in the air and clouded the windows. The sisters wisely decided to quickly return to their sleeping bags.

By 3 a.m. they still hadn't fallen asleep, so Agatha began telling Frannie about some of the trials she had read about in old newspaper clippings. Her voice seemed to fill the dark room, but then Frannie suddenly cut her off.

"Listen!" she said. "Did you hear it?"

Unfortunately, Agatha had heard *it*. The same *tap-tap-tap-tap* sound they had encountered before. Again, it came from the prisoner's box. Weirder still, it had kept time with her words and stopped abruptly just as Agatha had ceased talking.

She paused, having difficulty believing what she had heard. But her sister had heard it too. It couldn't have been her imagination, although she desperately willed it to be so.

 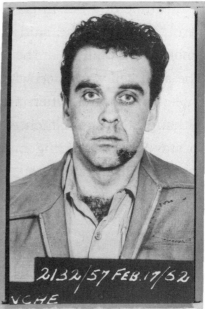

Arthur Lucas (left) and Ronald Turpin (right)

As a test, Agatha picked up where she had left off. Just one word, to see if the tapping sound was actually following her lead or if that had been some sort of coincidence.

Tap.

She said a second word.

Tap.

A third.

Tap.

And a fourth.

Tap.

She immediately stopped talking. Her heart felt like it was trying to pound straight through her chest and a cold sweat coated her clammy skin.

The sisters leapt to their feet and kicked their possessions across the floor as they fled from the room.

Frannie dug her fingernails into Agatha's arm as they ran. "My God," she said in a mad panic. "Look at the smoke." She pointed at the window to the judge's staircase. The stairwell was filled with mist.

It was 4 a.m. when they burst out onto the street. Although they hadn't lasted the night, they had managed to stay in the building much later than most. They had escaped with a tale to tell, but more importantly, they had escaped with their lives to live.

LiTTLE HAUNTED HOUSE ON THE PRAiRiE

Portage la Prairie, Manitoba

Twelve-year-old Chris McDermid flicked the light switch, plunging his room into darkness, and slid beneath his duvet. Although he was tired, he found it difficult to fall asleep. Chris's eyes slowly adjusted to the darkness as the sleepless minutes ticked by.

Chris and his parents had recently moved into the old house on 14th Street Northwest in Portage la Prairie, a rural community known for its agriculture. His room was spotless. In fact the entire house was spotless. Which made what happened that night all the more distressing.

As Chris waited for sleep to come, he was suddenly overcome by an unsettling feeling. Then he noticed something small crawling up the wall beside his bed. He blinked, refocused his eyes and realized it was a black spider. He rolled over and spotted another spider crawling across the floor. Then a third spider crept out of the shadows, followed by a fourth, a fifth, a sixth and on and on. Countless other spiders joined the first that had emerged, skittering in every direction, creeping across every surface. Then, as quickly as they had appeared, the spiders retreated back to wherever they had come from.

There was no sign of the insects the next day, yet the nighttime ordeal left young Chris feeling incredibly scared. But that was just the beginning. Soon he'd go from feeling scared to feeling like he was living in a nightmare.

Another night, not too long after, Chris turned off the light and saw something moving in his closet. He peered at his clothes and boxes, trying to figure out what had moved. Then a dark and dreadful spirit swelled within the closet, and Chris knew immediately that it was evil.

Frozen with fear and unable to call out for help, Chris watched helplessly as the spirit emerged from the closet, crossed the room and clambered onto his bed. It crawled up his body and perched on top of his chest, looking down at him silently and pinning the terrified boy to his mattress. The spirit soon disappeared, but it wasn't done terrorizing Chris for good. It returned many other nights after the boy turned out the lights.

The evil spirit had paranormal company in Chris's bedroom. Some nights, when the ghost remained in the closet, Chris would wake to find his bed surrounded by creatures with thick, matted hair long enough to reach their feet — feet that hovered above the ground. He yanked the bedsheets over his head and prayed for morning to come quickly, for he had discovered that when the sun rose, the creatures and ghosts were gone.

His parents never doubted their son's claims that his bedroom was haunted. They'd had their own dealings with the dead since moving into the house. Chris's father, Gordon, had kneeled to say his prayers one night when someone suddenly latched on to his back. Gordon spun around but found he was completely alone in the room.

Eighteen months after they moved in, Chris's mother, Nora, was getting to bed after a long day. It was 3 a.m. Not wanting to disturb her husband, she decided to sleep in a different bedroom. She collapsed on the bed and felt exhaustion whisking her away. But before she fell asleep she felt something: a hand on her leg. A second hand grabbed her other leg. There was no one there that Nora could see, but she could sense that whatever was touching her was a sinister entity. It crawled slowly up her body, trapping her under its weight just as it had done to Chris. But then the spirit tried to possess Nora's body. Nora fought through her blind terror and screamed for the spirit to get out.

The command worked. Nora felt the spirit slide down her rigid body and disappear. In fact, all of the ghosts left the house . . . or at least they were never seen by the McDermids again.

Eight years later the family moved out of the house without any further incidents. But Chris would never forget the horror of waking to find apparitions staring down at him in the middle of the night. An analytical person by nature, Chris, now in his mid-forties, still believes in ghosts. That's hardly surprising. When nightmares come to life, life becomes a nightmare.

BREAK A LEG, BREAK A NECK

Montreal, Quebec

House manager Layne Shutt was accustomed to late
nights spent alone in the Centaur Theatre. Part of his
job — one of the least savoury parts, truth be told — was
to walk around the old building after everyone had left to
ensure that all of the doors were closed and locked. One
night, after an extra-long day of work, Layne was in the
basement at 3:30 a.m. He started at one end of the long
hallway that stretched from one side of the building to the
other and made sure the many rooms were empty, lock-
ing each door as he made his way. First was the sound
room, followed by the costume shop with dresses and suits
draped over backs of chairs and hanging on mannequins.
Next were the green room and a couple of dressing rooms.
Layne continued into the prop shop, then the storage and

maintenance rooms. So far each room had been empty, just as Layne had expected. There was only one room left to check. He poked his head into the workshop and locked the door behind him, satisfied that there were no stragglers in the theatre's basement and that each of the doors was locked for the night.

He turned to walk back to the stairs and was completely unprepared for what he saw next.

Every single one of the supposedly locked doors was wide open.

Impossible. It was simply impossible. The doors couldn't be unlocked without the key that hung on Layne's key ring. And what's more, Layne was alone. Or was he? Layne was no longer so certain. Who had unlocked and opened all the doors without making a sound? Layne didn't stick around to find out. He quickly locked each of the doors again and sped out of the theatre before the ghost could open any more.

Built in 1903, the imposing building originally housed Canada's first stock exchange. Constructed of white stonework and fronted by six large pillars, many people take one look at the building and instantly believe it to be haunted. The Centaur Foundation for the Performing Arts purchased the building in 1969, and reports of ghost sightings began to surface soon after.

There are two popular theories about who the ghost of the Centaur Theatre is. Some people have reported seeing the ghost of a stockbroker in the basement, still working near the vaults left behind by the Montreal Stock Exchange. It's believed the former financier committed

Old Montreal Stock Exchange, now the Centaur Theatre

suicide in the building, but Layne puts his stock in the other theory. There used to be a telegraph in the Canadian Pacific Railway station across the cobblestone street, and the stock exchange hired young boys to run tickertape information back to the traders. The kids had to take the tapes upstairs to workers who were stationed on balconies, where they would scribble notes and numbers on chalkboards for everyone else to see. One day, a young boy tripped and fell over a balcony railing, falling down to the trading floor below. He broke his neck and died instantly.

So much of the paranormal activity — like the open doors in the basement — seems to be caused by a child who enjoys playing paranormal pranks, which is why

Layne believes the ghost that haunts the building is the boy who broke his neck.

Layne and many other staff members have seen a shadow run past as they prepare to leave for the night. Others have heard music playing from an unknown source.

On one occasion, a set designer grew agitated as he tried to paint some scenery on the main stage. He filled a can with paint and turned his back to complete another task. But when he turned back around, he was shocked to discover the can had somehow silently tipped over, spilling the paint across the stage. The mess took the man a long time to clean up. Once he had finished cleaning, he refilled the can, turned around for a moment, and then found the can tipped over once more. He couldn't believe his eyes, but his exasperation quickly gave way to fear.

The ghost of the Centaur Theatre might have already suffered life's final curtain call when he fell from the balcony and broke his neck, but now he haunts the building in a perpetual encore.

YOU CAN NEVER LEAVE

Georgina, Ontario

Toni and her husband moved to Georgina in 1991. They were drawn to the small-town way of life where everyone knew each other and you didn't have to lock your front door. The young couple wanted to raise a family, and the beautiful lakeside community less than an hour north of Toronto seemed to be the perfect place to settle down.

In 1993, the couple was blessed with a healthy baby boy, Jesse, and all was right with the world. The peace and quiet they had found in their home, however, was too good to be true.

Shortly after Jesse turned two, he became anxious, jumpy and easily startled. Before long he was scared all the time, particularly at bedtime, and he no longer wanted to sleep in his own room. His parents tried their best to soothe and reassure him, but nothing put him at ease. One night when Jesse was two and a half, he began to scream bloody murder from his room down the hall. His parents rushed into his room and found the poor boy sitting up in bed, shaking and sobbing uncontrollably. When he finally calmed down enough to explain what had upset him, he told his parents something that caught them completely off guard — something that chilled them to the bone.

"A man came through the wall," he said, pointing at the wall that divided his room from his closet. "He grabbed me. He tried to pull me through the wall but I banged against it. I couldn't go in! I couldn't go in!"

Toni stayed with Jesse in his room the rest of the night. She didn't see anything unusual. It must have been a bad dream.

But then, a few months later, Jesse ran into his parents' bedroom in the middle of the night and told them there was a woman with long black hair in the bathroom.

"I thought it was you," he told his mother quietly. "But it wasn't."

Even with this second sighting, Toni thought her son simply had an overactive imagination. She didn't believe in ghosts, and the thought that her house was haunted was laughable. But something happened two years later that wasn't funny at all.

Late one night Toni awoke, not from Jesse's night terrors, which she and her husband had grown accustomed to, but from the sudden appearance of two other boys. They were standing in her closet, which shared a wall with Jesse's closet. They were staring at her silently. One was six or seven years old, the other eleven or twelve. Both looked like farmers from a bygone era. The older boy wore a red plaid shirt and had wavy red hair and a very pale face. The younger boy wore blue jean overalls with no shirt and had short blond hair. They were both semi-transparent and glowed faintly blue.

Assuming it was a dream, Toni sat up and rubbed her eyes. But when she looked again the boys were still in her room — and they had moved closer to her bed. She blinked, and they were suddenly closer again. She looked away and, without warning, they were standing right beside her. She finally found her voice and screamed, waking her husband with a start. The boys disappeared immediately, and her husband saw nothing. But they had been there — Toni was certain of that. And now she knew that Jesse hadn't been dreaming or imagining things.

The ghosts kept on coming, as if Toni's house was some sort of dreadful destination for lost souls. One morning when he was five years old, Jesse woke early at 6 a.m. and went to the kitchen for a snack. Standing at the other end of the room was a man in a sheriff's hat who approached the frightened boy before disappearing.

On a different day her husband, still skeptical of his wife's and son's claims that their house was haunted, saw a man's face appear and disappear in the doorway between the living room and kitchen. After that, he was a skeptic no more. Extended family members — brothers and sisters, nephews and nieces — felt a bad vibe in Jesse's bedroom. Most refused to sleep in the house, but those who didn't heard whispered conversations within the walls. Toni once watched her deceased grandmother walk out of her closet, cross the room to the bed and lay a large bouquet of roses on her husband's chest. As soon as the flowers touched him, his eyes flew open and he began to choke, unable to breathe. Both Grandma and the flowers vanished immediately and it took Toni's husband a long time before he could breathe properly again.

One evening Toni went into the kitchen to get a drink. As soon as she entered the room, a glass levitated out of the sink, floated in circles for a moment and then shattered into dozens of pieces that rained to the floor. Toni was understandably shocked, but she found some solace in the fact that both her parents and her sister-in-law had seen the paranormal activity, and her brother had heard it.

"You're right," her father said, giving credence to Toni's claims, "there *are* spirits in this house."

On another occasion, Toni and her family were away for a weekend camping trip at Sibbald Point Provincial Park, not too far from her home. There was a terrible thunderstorm on the Friday night. When Toni returned with Jesse on Sunday, her new next-door neighbour introduced himself and said he was excited that Toni had children.

"They can play with my eight-year-old daughter," he said.

When Toni informed him that she only had a son, the man told her on the Friday night he'd seen three children — a six-year-old boy, a nine-year-old girl and a fourteen-year-old boy — run around the house in the rain and go through her front door.

When Toni said that was impossible, the man joked,

"Oh, maybe you have ghosts." He laughed. Toni didn't.

Thus far, the ghosts who had appeared in her house hadn't seemed to have ill or evil intent. That would soon change.

First up was the spirit Toni called the Peek-a-Boo Boy. The first time he made his mischievous presence known was shortly after Toni and her husband had split up and her husband had moved out. Toni was up late on her computer in the living room and Jesse, now eight, had gone to bed earlier in the evening. Out of the corner of her eye, Toni saw someone run through the hall. She looked up from the monitor. No one was there, but she heard the faint sound of childish giggling.

Tee, hee, hee.

"Go back to bed," she yelled to Jesse. When there was no response, she turned her attention back to her computer.

After a moment, she heard it again. *Tee, hee, hee.*

This time the laughter had come from behind the couch. She spun around, but once again she didn't see a soul. She checked on Jesse — he was sound asleep in his bed, so she returned to the couch and her computer.

Shortly after, she saw movement out of the corner of her eye and looked up. Peering over the back of the couch was a seven-year-old boy with a blond bowl cut. He ducked down when Toni spotted him. She leapt off the couch but the boy had disappeared. Toni raced around the house and turned on every single light in a desperate attempt to make herself feel more comfortable. It worked, if only a little. But the Peek-a-Boo Boy continued to spy on her for years, both day and night. More unnerving than his presence was the creepy sound of his laughter as he ran, hid and watched: *Tee, hee, hee.*

One night shortly after Toni started seeing the Peek-a-Boo Boy, she had the most terrifying experience yet. It was a hot summer night, and as a treat, Jesse was up late watching television in her room while Toni was down the hall in the living room.

Through the open bedroom door, Jesse said, "Good night, Mommy. Love you." He turned off the television and the bedroom light.

Silence followed.

Ten minutes later, he began to scream at the top of his lungs. Toni ran to the doorway, reached her hand into the dark room and turned on the light switch. As soon as the light was on, Toni was met with a horrible sight. Jesse was pinned against the window by some invisible force, his feet thirty centimetres above the top of the mattress. His eyes were wide with terror and sweat poured down his flushed cheeks.

"You're not my mommy!" he shouted — not at Toni, but at something he could see in the closet. "You're not my mommy!"

Toni tried to enter the room but couldn't — there was some sort of invisible force holding her back, not unlike whatever energy was holding her son up against the window.

"Let go of my son!" she shouted, her eyes darting wildly between Jesse and her closet.

Jesse continued to repeat his frantic cry. "You're not my

mommy! You're not my mommy! You're not my mommy!"

Blinded by panic and on the verge of passing out from stress and terror, Toni summoned all her remaining strength and bellowed, "LET MY SON GO!"

It worked. She was released from her invisible chains, and Jesse flew across the room into her arms. The entire house immediately turned ice cold, so cold that they could see their breath despite the fact that it was the middle of summer. They ran and hid in the living room. It took some time before Jesse could tell Toni what he had seen in the closet.

"It was a pale lady with long black hair, dripping wet," he said. When he had woken up and seen her, the woman told him, "Come with me. I'm your mommy."

Needless to say, Toni was incredibly relieved that Jesse had not set foot in the closet with the black-haired ghost. However, this traumatic event took place more than fifteen years ago and she hasn't been able to spend a night in her bedroom since. Instead, she sleeps on the living room couch and only runs into her bedroom each morning to grab some clothes for the day. Every now and again, the closet's doorknob rattles as she passes.

But the couch isn't always a safe place to sleep. Toni will never be able to forget the night when Jesse was staying over at a friend's house. It was 3 a.m. Toni was asleep, facing the back of the couch. Someone tapped her shoulder and said, "Mom."

At first Toni thought she was dreaming. She woke a little but didn't open her eyes, and tried to go back to sleep.

Tap, tap, tap.

"Mom!"

Toni spun over on her other side and saw she wasn't alone. But it wasn't Jesse. There was a teenage boy standing beside the couch, looking down on her. Well, "looking" might not be the most precise term to describe what he was doing, since his eyes had been gouged from their sockets. Bloody tears ran down the boy's cheeks.

Toni screamed and the eyeless boy disappeared.

Why does Toni continue to live in what is quite possibly the most terrifying house in the country? Why didn't she move years ago?

The short answer is she can't. The longer answer is she tried to leave, back in 2002, and it didn't go well. She'd had enough and she was concerned for her son's safety, so she put the house on the market for a reasonable price, hoping to sell quickly and move on, restarting her life in a new location. And fate seemed to be smiling on her as a contractor made an offer on the house with plans to renovate and resell it. All he required before finalizing the deal was a home inspection. Toni was thrilled.

Toni let him in and needed to leave to run some errands, so she asked the contractor to ensure he closed the crawlspace door, which was in Jesse's closet, when he was done inspecting the pipes in the crawlspace. She didn't want her pets to accidentally fall through the opening while she was away. She also asked him to close and lock the front door. He promised to do so and she left.

An hour later, Toni returned.

Her front door was wide open.

"Hello?" she called as she walked inside, more than

a little annoyed. There was no answer, only silence. As she passed her bedroom she noticed a teddy bear her ex-husband had given her for Valentine's Day a few years back. Oddly, it had been turned upside down on the chair where it sat. Then Toni saw the contractor's extension cord running from an outlet in the kitchen to Jesse's bedroom. She followed the cord to the closet and discovered the trap door to the crawlspace was open too.

Unbelievable, Toni thought. *He left both doors wide open.*

The cord led to a light the contractor had used to see in the dark sublevel. The light was still on. Scattered across the floor of Jesse's room were the contractor's tools — screwdrivers, wrenches and a hammer. And odder yet: like the teddy bear, all of her son's stuffed animals had been turned upside down on his bed.

Toni's phone rang, scaring the living daylights out of her. It was the real estate agent. She had some unfortunate news.

"I'm sorry," she said, "but the sale has fallen through. He's not interested."

Toni couldn't believe what she was hearing. She told the agent that the contractor left both doors open and even left all his tools in her house. "What happened?" she asked.

"I don't know; he wouldn't say," the agent said. "All he did say was, and I quote, 'Tell the lady she's crazy for living there and she can keep all my tools.'"

Why Toni's house is such a hotbed for paranormal activity, like the question of what the contractor saw in the crawlspace, is a complete mystery. She did a little digging recently and obtained official records about her house's history. The earliest record she could find was from 1950, and it revealed that the house was owned by the Supreme Court of Canada. The record also showed the dates that the house was sold between 1950 and 1991, the year Toni purchased it with her ex-husband. In those forty-one years, dozens of people bought the house and quickly resold it. The longest anyone was able to live there was two years. Some got rid of it as quickly as three months after moving in.

That Toni has lived there so long is a testament to her mental fortitude and resolve. But after the failed attempt to sell the house, she feels the spirits will never let her leave.

DEADMAN'S ISLAND

Vancouver, British Columbia

Deadman's Island seems forever cursed to be the final resting place for countless lost souls. Given its bloody history, this should surprise no one. In fact, it's believed by some to be the most haunted island in North America.

In poet and author E. Pauline Johnson's 1911 book, *Legends of Vancouver,* Johnson wrote about a conflict that took place on the island, as described to her by Chief Joe Capilano. Two First Nations groups, one from the north and one from the south, fought to claim ownership of Deadman's Island. The battle was drawn-out and fierce, and many people died.

Later, in the 1860s, the local government offered to sell the island to one of the city's early pioneers, Samuel Brighouse. His partner, John Morton, rowed a boat to the

Deadman's Island

island to explore it. He was well aware of the island's dark reputation, but he wasn't prepared for what he discovered there. He stumbled upon a red cedar box, sealed shut and nestled among bushes. It was, Morton was sickened to discover, the same size and shape as a coffin. He wondered if there was a corpse inside, but then why wouldn't it be buried? As he moved deeper toward the heart of the island his dread grew. There was a second box, and a third, a fourth, a fifth . . . He passed hundreds of boxes, and not all were on the ground. Some were in the trees, precariously perched on branches. He reached up and touched one as if to make sure it wasn't a dark figment of his imagination. It was real, all right. All too real. It crumbled when he poked it and a pile of human bones and remains showered down on him. Needless to say, Morton and Brighouse did not purchase Deadman's Island.

Thirty years later, Vancouver was afflicted with a smallpox outbreak. The sick multiplied and the bodies piled up as the disease spread rapidly through the city streets. In an attempt to contain the spread of smallpox, the government decided to use Deadman's Island as a quarantine zone. The sick were sent there to get better and return to the city, or die and remain on the island forever. Bodies were buried in makeshift graves all over the island, with little more than cedar sticks marking their final resting places, and trees filling in for tombstones.

On May 31, 1909, Vancouver police officers huddled together around a fire pit, casting nervous glances into the woods that surrounded them. Every snapping twig, every moving shadow, every pair of lurking eyes reflecting light in the darkness caused them to jump. The suffocating sense of nervousness that permeated the air was hardly a shock to anyone gathered there that night; the men knew the soil beneath their feet was said to be soaked in blood.

The police officers were there to prevent Theodore Ludgate, an American industrialist, and E. L. Kinman, managing director of the Island Deck and Warehouse Company, from building a sawmill and cutting down trees on the island. Ten years before, Ludgate had signed a deal with the federal government to lease the island for the paltry sum of $500 for twenty-five years. When Vancouver citizens and local government found out about the deal, they were furious. Deadman's Island was a key part of Stanley Park, an area of immeasurable natural beauty that was quickly becoming one of Vancouver's biggest tourist attractions.

And so, when local authorities were tipped off that Kinman's men were planning on logging the island in late May and early June, the police camped out overnight to prevent that from happening.

Some officers quickly wished they hadn't been assigned the task.

The sounds of the wind blowing through the trees and wildlife creeping through the bush were replaced by something far more ominous. The police officers heard the rattling of bones, as if the island's corpses had been reanimated. That was bad enough, but then the skeletons took up a wild, shrieking chorus that tore through the night and sent shivers down the police officers' spines. In an attempt to calm and comfort his men, Police Chief Chamberlain walked amongst them and recommended that they light and carry torches, to bolster their courage and to fend off the volatile spirits. After a restless night, Kinman and his loggers were eventually caught and arrested. Following the logging dispute, the island was granted to the navy and became the HMCS Discovery naval base. Naval reservists receive their training on the island, which has had restricted access since 1942, and it wasn't long before the navy learned that they weren't alone. Many sailors have had eerie encounters while stationed on the island overnight, including hearing the sound of furniture moving in the buildings when no one else is there, and seeing an odd glow through the trees that slowly shifts into human form and floats out of sight.

In 2007, one woman was trailed all over the island by a presence she couldn't see. As she tried to get away from the spirit, it whispered in her ear, exhaled in her hair and poked and prodded her back. She had the overwhelming feeling that it was a malicious spirit that wanted to use her as a living host. She evaded the ghost and left the island, never to return.

This is a recurring theme of the island. Most people who visit — even those brave enough to serve and protect the country in the police force or navy — are more than happy to leave Deadman's Island to the dead men who haunt it.

THE HEAD SCRATCHER

Moncton, New Brunswick

At the end of a long day, a precocious fourth grader knelt beside her bed, clasped her hands and closed her eyes in prayer. She had performed this ritual every night for as long as she could remember. She finished her prayer, turned out the light and slipped beneath the covers of her bed.

At three o'clock she woke up suddenly and opened her eyes wide. She stared at her clock for a few minutes, not tired at all, wondering what had woken her. And then she found out.

Something was scratching the top of her head from front to back. She was certain that it was a fingernail. Too afraid to look, the girl brushed the finger aside and tried to convince herself that she had dreamt it, or maybe she had rubbed her head against the bedpost. But she knew what she felt was real.

If the scratching had happened only that one night, she might have been able to forget about it and move on. But the spirit had no plans to leave the poor girl alone. The next night, the girl said her prayers, climbed back into bed and fell asleep. Near three o'clock, she woke up again. And then, a few moments later, something scratched her scalp, slowly and painfully. The following night, it happened again — and the next night, and the night after that. The ghostly attack happened each and every night for ten nights in a row before the girl came up with a plan.

First, the girl decided she would stay awake through the night to see with her own eyes what was happening and to ensure she wasn't going crazy. But soon her eyelids began to droop and she fell into another restless slumber, a slumber that was once again broken by the sharp scratching digging into her skin.

The following night she made a desperate pact with herself: the next time she was awakened by the scratching she would pinch her arms to make sure she wasn't suffering from a recurring nightmare. Sure enough, she was woken again at three o'clock, so she pinched herself hard. But she wasn't dreaming — she was fully awake, and the scratching continued. To make matters worse, the sensation became more painful each night. The presence was growing darker the longer the attacks wore on. Something had to be done to stop it.

She didn't want to involve her parents — she didn't know how to explain what was happening to her — so she decided she would confront her attacker herself. Her new plan was to grab at it and hope that she could somehow stop it from hurting her ever again. She was terrified by the thought of what might happen to her, but she didn't know what else to do.

With this desperate idea on her mind, she said her prayers and crawled under the sheets. She fell asleep. When she awoke, the scratching was harder than ever. The moment it started she reached behind her head and grabbed her attacker. As she had feared at the very beginning of this ordeal, it was a long bony finger that straightened in surprise once she held it. She sat up in bed and spun around to see who had been hurting her for so long. She wasn't prepared for what she saw next.

A large black shadow — blacker than black — rose up from the floor behind her bed, spread out in the air and towered above her menacingly. It had no features, no face, just ten bony fingers and ten long nails.

The girl screamed, released her grip on its finger and ran to her parents' bedroom. She jumped in their bed and, through tears and sobs, finally told them about the ordeal she had been suffering through for weeks. Her father searched her room but found nothing out of the ordinary, not even under her bed.

Luckily, the dark spirit never returned after that night, but it haunted the girl's dreams for a long time.

THE PEOPLE UPSTAIRS

Bonavista, Newfoundland and Labrador

One day in 1999, Susan Fabres and her friend were late for work and considered taking a shortcut through the Bradley House property to save time. Susan had heard stories claiming that Bradley House was haunted, and she was understandably hesitant to pass through its yard. But her friend insisted and Susan eventually relented.

As they neared the house, Susan stopped dead in her tracks and looked up at a window. She had an odd feeling, as if she was being watched from above. A cold chill cut through her skin and seized her bones. That's when she looked past her friend and saw a man in old-fashioned clothing suddenly appear behind her. When her friend turned and saw the man too, Susan knew she wasn't

Bradley House

imagining things. They took off as fast as their legs could carry them.

It's interesting that Susan had a bad feeling when she looked at the second-floor window. Many passersby have looked at the same window at night and seen a bright light coming from the room, but the building is unoccupied and has no electricity. Upon closer inspection, people have seen an old woman rocking in a chair by the window, sometimes minding her own business, other times peering out into the darkness of the neighbourhood.

The old woman is believed to be the grandmother of Gordon Bradley. Gordon was one of the last people to live in Bradley House before it was donated to the government in 1981 and became a museum that depicts early Newfoundland life. He was also one of the founding members of the Bonavista Historical Society, and he had first-hand knowledge of the town's ghostly history.

Early one morning when Gordon was a child, he found his mother sitting alone in the kitchen. They chatted for a little while before his mother's demeanour changed and she whispered, "They were at it again last night."

Not sure what she meant, Gordon asked, "Who was at what, Mother?"

His mother looked young Gordon in the eye and said, "The people who live upstairs."

She told Gordon that she had heard the sounds of a large and boisterous party: people walking, voices talking, laughing and singing and even doors opening and slamming shut. Gordon's mother had waited downstairs for the commotion to die down and eventually stop before going upstairs to bed. She was exhausted by the time her head hit the pillow, so she fell asleep almost immediately.

Deborah Way, site manager of Matthew Legacy Inc., an organization that promotes Bonavista's local heritage, is straightforward when discussing the area. She believes that it's a haunted place, and she's not the only one to hold such a blunt opinion — she claims that many other locals feel the same. In fact, Deborah takes it a step farther and states that the citizens of Bonavista don't just feel that their hometown is haunted — they *know* it.

Susan Fabres and her friend knew it, as did Gordon

Bradley and his mother. And once you know beyond a shadow of a doubt that something haunts one of your town's most well-known historical sites, it's nearly impossible to forget.

NO SLEEP FOR THE DEAD

Georgetown, Ontario

Virginia moved into a new home on Maple Avenue, a nice house with a happy vibe. It was cozy and warm with an inviting wraparound porch, a bright and cheerful red front door and a rock path that meandered through a flower garden in the front yard.

Little did Virginia know that when she moved in, someone refused to move out.

The house was built in 1854 and was once owned by a minister who used to hold church services in the backyard. There was only one small window looking out on the front yard from the second floor, so houseguests couldn't see much of the upper level as they arrived. That was for the best. The guests wouldn't have liked what they might have seen.

One night not long after she moved into the house with her husband and daughter, Virginia was all alone. She was on the main floor, enjoying a calm and peaceful evening, when suddenly she heard someone running down the upstairs hall. The tapping sound of shoes on the floor was very clear and distinct. Then she heard every door slam at once with a colossal bang. This was followed by a brief moment of dead silence, and then the unnerving sound of a little girl giggling.

Although she didn't see the child, Virginia formed a clear picture of her in her mind. And she wasn't just laughing to herself — the girl was laughing *at* Virginia. It was like the girl got a thrill out of taunting and terrorizing the woman.

The girl ran up and down the hall quite regularly for two years, slamming doors and laughing — always laughing — as if at a private joke. She tormented Virginia by creating a racket and laughing about it day and night, but she was only active when Virginia was alone in the house. Neither her husband nor her daughter ever heard anything unusual.

Then one day a woman from Virginia's church told her in a hushed whisper that a girl who used to live in the house had died on the second floor long ago. She was ten or twelve years old at the time of her death, and the description the churchgoer gave of the dead girl was an identical match to the image Virginia had in her head.

Although Virginia was the only person in her immediate family who experienced the ghost girl's antics, her niece and her sister Lindsay knew something wasn't right

Virginia's house on Maple Avenue

in the house from the very first time they visited. Virginia's niece didn't like playing upstairs. She was overwhelmed by the unsettling vibe that she and her cousin weren't alone on the second floor. And she flat out refused to stay in the house overnight, always insisting on returning to her own house before the hour grew late.

Lindsay, on the other hand, did spend the night. And when she stayed over, she slept upstairs. Well, she tried her best but she got very little sleep.

During one visit, Lindsay was in one room while Virginia and her husband were in another. Virginia's daughter was at a sleepover. Nothing seemed amiss until 2 a.m. Lindsay was awoken by a very loud sound of feet pounding up and down the hallway. First from one end to the other. *Bang, bang, bang, bang, bang!* Then back again. *Bang, bang, bang, bang, bang!* Fifteen minutes passed, then thirty, then forty-five, and whoever was in the hallway kept running back and forth, back and forth. When the clock read three o'clock and the disturbance hadn't stopped, Lindsay decided enough was enough. She assumed the source of the sound was her sister's cat, Skye. So she got out of bed, walked across the room, opened the door and peered into the hallway.

There was no sign of Skye. There was no sign of anyone. But the sound of running had continued right up to the moment she had opened the door. She walked down the empty hall to the bathroom, then returned to her room.

As she lay back down, Lindsay began to wonder if she had dreamt the sound. But before she reached a conclusion, someone started running down the hallway again.

"Will you give it a rest!" Lindsay shouted, startling even herself. She hadn't planned on yelling; it had just slipped out. At least it worked. The noise stopped — for a moment. But then it picked right back up again.

First one way. *Bang, bang, bang, bang, bang!* Then the other. *Bang, bang, bang, bang, bang!*

"Shut up!" Lindsay screamed.

This outburst finally stopped the madness for good. Lindsay slowly fell back asleep and wasn't woken again the rest of the night.

When she got out of bed early the next morning, she made her sleepy way downstairs. Her brother-in-law,

Virginia's husband, was sitting at the breakfast table.

After exchanging pleasantries and chatting for a while, Lindsay said, "The cat went crazy during the night," and explained what had happened.

Her brother-in-law looked at Lindsay with a blank expression for a while, as if he was trying to work something out in his mind. Finally he informed Lindsay that the cat had spent the entire night downstairs. Skye was old and unable to climb the stairs, much less run around causing a commotion. Furthermore, the cat wore a bell on her collar.

"Did you hear a bell at any point during the night?" he asked.

Lindsay shook her head. She had not. But if it hadn't been Skye, then who was it?

Virginia knew her sister had been kept awake by the laughing girl. The dead girl. The girl who isn't capable of resting in peace despite how cozy and comforting the house may be.

LOST IN THE WOODS

Wood Buffalo National Park, Alberta

Golden shafts of early-morning sunlight broke through the forest canopy, bathing the woods in a warm glow. Birds chirped and a gentle breeze ruffled leaves. A deer walked silently through the trees, eating moss and lichen from the forest floor. Cool water flowed through a gentle creek.

Three children raced through the woods, streams of sweat and tears running down their cheeks. Their eyes were wide with panic and their breathing was rapid. Denise, the oldest at thirteen, whipped her head from side to side, frantically looking for something — anything — that would lead her and her two younger siblings back to safety. Along with eleven-year-old Lucille and six-year-old Jerome, Denise had silently crept out of her family's tent early that morning while their parents were still asleep.

They loved the outdoors and wanted to go for a special hike — just kids. They thought they'd have a great time and be back before their parents even knew they had left.

On both counts they were dead wrong.

Before long they were completely disoriented in the dense forest of northern Alberta's Wood Buffalo National Park. Which direction was north? Where had they come from? The kids had no idea. They were completely lost.

Panic set in. Little Jerome began to cry. Every second that ticked by felt like a minute, and every minute that passed felt like an eternity. The longer they spent alone in the woods, the greater their odds became of never finding their way back to safety. The situation was dire and grim.

But then Denise stopped and made her siblings stop too. Their parents were outdoorsy people and had taught the children basic survival skills just in case they ever found themselves in this type of predicament. She remembered her parents telling her to find shelter and stay in one place, making it easier for a search party to find her. The kids found some low-hanging, thick vegetation and settled in, hoping someone would find them before nightfall.

Back at the campsite, their parents, Mr. and Mrs. Lacroix, woke up to an empty tent. At first they assumed the kids must be playing nearby. But there was no sign of them anywhere. Mr. Lacroix walked a circle in the woods surrounding their tent. He saw nothing. Mrs. Lacroix strained her ears hoping to hear their distant chatter and laughter. She heard nothing.

"Denise?" Mr. Lacroix called. "Lucille?"

"Jerome?" Mrs. Lacroix added.

No one answered.

With a sickening feeling swelling in their guts, the parents realized their children were gone. Nightmare scenarios played out in their minds, each one more deadly and frightening than the last.

The dark irony that they had planned this camping trip to get their minds off of a death did not escape their notice. Earlier that summer in 1958, the family's beloved collie dog, Ruffles, had died. The parents were upset by the loss, but the children were devastated, nearly inconsolable. They had lost a family member, and the five weeks that followed were cloaked in grief. But as soon as they had reached Wood Buffalo National Park, their spirits lifted. The camp-out was exactly what the grieving family needed to heal and move on.

Desperate to find his children, Mr. Lacroix jumped into his car and drove to the nearest settlement. He told everyone he could find what had happened, and convinced a small group of strangers to follow him back to the campsite to help look for Denise, Lucille and Jerome. He was hopeful he'd return to find his children safe and sound in his wife's arms, but no such luck. Mrs. Lacroix was still alone.

The search party fanned out into the woods. Mrs. Lacroix remained at the campsite in case her children returned while her husband pushed deeper and deeper into the woods.

As morning gave way to afternoon and afternoon began to wane, a heavy sense of dismay took root in the hearts of everyone who had assembled to search for the Lacroix children. No clue to their whereabouts had been found.

Far away from the rest of the search party, a man named Bob stopped and rubbed his eyes. He thought he had seen something pass him, a shadowy blur of movement. Then a dog walked around a tree and stared at the man. It was a collie wearing a collar and tag. Bob thought that was odd. The dog was clearly someone's pet, but he couldn't recall anyone bringing the animal with them on the search.

The collie slowly approached and allowed Bob to pet him. Bob grabbed the dog's tag and read it. The dog's name was engraved on the metal tag.

Ruffles.

Ruffles walked a few paces away from Bob and turned to face him. When Bob didn't follow, Ruffles looped back, walked around Bob and walked away again. Bob got the feeling that the dog was trying to lead him somewhere. Since the search had yet to turn anything up, Bob figured it couldn't hurt to follow the dog, at least for a little while. The searchers they passed joined Bob and Ruffles, and the dog's group slowly began to grow.

Then, as suddenly as he had appeared in the woods, the dog disappeared.

"Ruffles, come here," Bob called, assuming they had simply lost sight of the dog for a moment. He had to be around somewhere. "Come, Ruffles!"

The dog didn't return, and the more Bob thought about the encounter, the more he began to think that there was something not quite right about it.

A short distance away, the three Lacroix children were

still holding each other tightly under the vegetation, sick with worry and fear. They heard a stranger's voice calling for their deceased pet, Ruffles. For a confused and disoriented moment, Denise thought that she and her siblings had died and were about to be reunited with Ruffles. Young Jerome, however, seemed to catch on sooner than his older sisters and called out for Ruffles too. The search party heard the boy and the children were found. They were soon reunited with their relieved parents.

When Bob shared how he had found the children, the Lacroix family knew the ghost of their deceased pet had sensed the children were in mortal danger and had materialized in the woods to rescue them. Ruffles proved that dogs truly are man's best friend, and it's a friendship that will never die.

PHOTO CREDITS

Page 10: City of Winnipeg
Page 15: Courtesy of the Maritime Museum of the Atlantic, M61.54
Page 34: Topley Studio Fonds/Library and Archives Canada/
PA-033577
Page 44: Salt Spring Island Archives with permission from the
Harbour House Hotel
Page 46: Courtesy of Gulf Islands Driftwood
Page 55: Pat Arrington/Niagara-on-the-Lake Public Library
Page 63: Tanya Plonka
Page 69: Alison Cornford-Matheson/Dreamstime
Page 75: Metro Toronto Police/Courtesy of Robert J. Hoshowsky
Page 83: Albertype Company/Library and Archives Canada/
PA-032284
Page 96: J. Wood Laing/City of Vancouver Archives
Page 104: Provincial Historic Sites, Newfoundland & Labrador,
Canada
Page 109: Courtesy of K. V. Jones

Joel A. Sutherland is an author and librarian. He is the author of several books in the Haunted Canada series, as well as *Be a Writing Superstar, Summer's End* and *Frozen Blood*, a horror novel that was nominated for the Bram Stoker Award. His short fiction has appeared in many anthologies and magazines, alongside the likes of Stephen King and Neil Gaiman. He has been a juror for the John Spray Mystery Award and the Monica Hughes Award for Science Fiction and Fantasy.

He appeared as "The Barbarian Librarian" on the Canadian edition of the hit television show *Wipeout,* making it all the way to the third round and proving that librarians can be just as tough and crazy as anyone else.

Joel lives with his family in southeastern Ontario, where he is always on the lookout for ghosts.

HAUNTED CANADA

Read the whole chilling series.

978-0-7791-1410-8

978-0-439-96122-6

978-0-439-93777-1

978-1-4431-2893-3

978-1-4431-3929-8

978-1-4431-4878-8

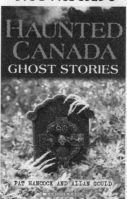

978-1-4431-2894-0

For Haunted Canada bonus material,
visit www.scholastic.ca/hauntedcanada.